AGAINST MEDICAL ADVICE

AGAINST MEDICAL ADVICE

ADVICE

OVERCOMING STROKE DURING DIVORCE

Simone L. Gisondi, CHNC

AGAINST MEDICAL ADVICE

Copyright © 2021 by Simone L. Gisondi

Cover Design: Melissa Desveaux, Birgit Itse

Editor: Lee Zehnder Ross; Vivie Bishop

Published in USA

Print ISBN: 979-8-9853873-1-5

Visit Amazon.com/Amazon.ca and the author's website SimoneGisondi.com for more details and for how to purchase this book.

Dedication to my heros ♡

To my children who are hands down God's greatest masterpieces and without whom life would just be empty and tasteless.

To Frank whose support never ceased and who put up with me since day one.

To mom and dad who taught me unimaginable strength, all about sacrifice, about giving selflessly and to always play life by my own rules.

Appreciation ♡

A Few Words of Thanks from your Deeply Grateful Author

The book you have in your hands right has been my dream for years, so it is in every sense a dream come true. Thank you for picking it up.

While a book is written by the author, it takes a village as they say, to bring it into existence. And a village it was that brought this one to you.

I never guessed how far I would have to travel into the depths of myself and how many people would be part of this journey and the birth of this book.

Like all my fellow authors I am forever indebted to so many but the first thank you goes to you God, first for blessing me with my unique, crazy spirit and for giving me this incredible experience so that I can write my first book and be able to tell THE STORY.

I am forever grateful to you Marcus and Roman, you two are my heroes. Without your immense love I would've surely perished. You two will always be the love and light of my existence. The words "I love and adore you" pale in comparison to the immensity of the love I feel for you both.

Thank you Frank, for your incredible heart, your endless support, your generosity, your kindness, your patience and for always being there for me through the hardships of life. To say that you have been and are the anchor of the family we created together is a gross understatement. You have blessed me beyond measure.

I will never be able to repay you mom and dad for your endless love, for the life lessons you taught me, for the sacrifices you both made for me, and for being the most exemplary human beings in ways I can't even express. I am lucky to be a product of you two - the strongest people I know.

Thank you, Reni and Lina, for being like second mothers to my amazing children and for your endless help no matter what crazy thing I would do, like move AGAIN.

Jowita, thank you for your never-ending support and friendship, for your generosity and for being part of my crazy life for two decades. I am deeply grateful to you for all that you are and for spending time in a place I know you would never be caught in, just to help and encourage me during the hardest time of my life. Words can't capture how grateful I am for you.

Loretta, I am so thankful for all you have taught me about being an author. You've inspired me more than you know.

Birgit, this book would've never come to be an actual book in the hands of readers had it not been for you, your patience, your expertise, your support, your guidance, your help and your belief in me as an author. You have no idea how much you inspired me to see this book published.

Lee, thank you for all your priceless advice and for the time you took to get this book to be what it is.

Vivie, thank you for gifting me your amazing brilliance and your precious time. You have no idea what it means to me to have such incredible words of encouragement coming from someone of your literary caliber. I am forever indebted to you and Hans just for being you and for being the example of love and passion. Thank you both for blessing me. "Good catch Vivie."

Cris, I am so grateful for your incredible generosity, kindness, patience and help in search of the perfect title. You are amazing beyond words.

Thank you, Russ, for being such an amazing mentor. Thank you for your kindness, your generosity and for making the insanely long treks during Canadian winters just to help me.

Thank you Elisabeth, Jamie, Debra, Tatijana, Marianne, Indepreet, Chavi, Videshi and Greg, for your precious time and for reading the manuscript. Your advice is so incredibly valuable in making this book a quality piece of literature. I owe each of you immensely.

Thank you Melissa, for being so incredibly patient with me, for everything you taught me and for helping make this dream of mine come true on such short notice. You are beyond amazing for putting up with my endless requests for revisions. I could not have pulled this off without you and your expertise.

Thank you, reader, for picking up this book, for believing in reading and in the magic of books.

Reviews ♡

I have known Simone since we have studied holistic nutrition together. I had known that she went through a serious health crisis but I did not realize the depth of it.

In this story Simone shows you that nothing and nobody can scare you! Life can only expose the fear that is already inside you!

As I went through my own struggles, I found myself in her story; I feel like she wrote this book and personal deep thoughts just for me, to give me strength and hope. I am very grateful for her bravery to publish her own recovery and all she shares in this eye-opening story.

You want to read this book. And then, ask yourself some serious questions.

Elisabeth Stefanic

***

Simone's book is a great example for those who push through life without being attuned to their subconscious mind that is always there to provide guidance and answers when needed. And if ignored and pushed aside, it will always give you a valuable lesson that may not always be the most pleasant

Magdalena Lewicki

While troubled times last, they cannot defeat us. We are always in control of the choices we make. As humans we have been blessed with the capacity to choose and move on from difficult situations gracefully with smiles on our faces and hope for the future in our hearts. It does not mean there will not be tough times in the future. Simone's story illustrates that we are capable of taking strides and changing our circumstances while learning how to embrace the toughest moments. The courage she has to show everyone what it takes to reclaim your health and your life is powerful, inspiring and moving.

Inderpreet Kalra

***

AGAINST MEDICAL ADVICE is an essential and convincingly thought provocative book. The insight of Simone Gisondi's experience of a stroke as a young, fit, and healthy female is simply incredible and a must read. I literally inhaled her book!

Her strength, positive thinking and trusting her inner voice have proven how powerful the mind is. Simone is an amazing individual who has taken her life in her own hands ...*AGAINST MEDICAL ADVICE*... by using her infinite potential, survived and transformed her life.

There are several aspects I can relate in Simone's book such as starting all over after divorce or obviously using the power of positive thinking and beyond, as well as healing yourself from the inside out in a holistic way. What a remarkable inspiration!

Marianne Weiss

A profound, true life story that will inspire in anyone who reads it, an attitude of "Anything Is Possible!" even against the odds. Simone exudes a strong will and determination coupled with a growing faith in God, which without a doubt creates natural healing; physically, mentally and spiritually. This book gives all the feels!!!

I definitely felt as if I was inside the book when reading it ~ I was feeling everything ... all the emotions!

I knew about Simone's stroke, but reading the book filled in many other pieces, like what she experienced during it (the lightning description) and what was happening around with her family. Many times I got choked up with tears and other times I busted out with laughter as I could totally see and hear her interactions with various individuals (friend at party, Frank, doctor, nurse) as if I was there in person.

Her go-getter attitude inspires me and I definitely remind myself when I'm struggling with things. Although everybody is different (their level of push or speed), we are all the same, as in we can do anything if we put our minds to it.

Tatijana Kulis-Sousa

***

This book was such an easy read! Simone's writing style grabbed my attention from the first page.

I was engaged quickly and read the whole book in 3 sit down sessions. She explained her thoughts so well and she has a good way to play up the strong side that pushed her through the events of the stroke.

The explanations of her home and the hospital helped me visualize what she was experiencing the whole time.

She leaves you with the belief that much success is always to come. I must say that she has peaked my interest to gain more awareness about natural healing methods vs traditional medicine!

James McNamara

***

Contents ♡

Foreword

Over the years as a therapist and consultant to organizations I have had the privilege of working with so many wonderful individuals all at different stages. I must say that when I met and spent some time with Simone I was deeply impressed and impacted by her passion, zeal for life and deep desire to positively impact others. I didn't know why and was curious to find out.

I had been working as a consultant to a health and wellness chain and spent time on a regular basis with the managers of the various stores in a performance and team building capacity. It was on my first visit to one of the Toronto stores that I met Simone. Immediately her presence and passion were infectious. Here was no ordinary woman but one who loved life and people and was committed to health and wellness.

It was on my third visit over a coffee that Simone began to share with me her journey that unfolds in this book. This is not just another story of struggle, but a story of love, passion, soul, emotion. In these pages is the heart and example of what it means to defy the odds, to overcome adversity and to make a difference.

It's no secret we are in times of great uncertainty, chaos, confusion, a time where anxiety and unrest is at an all-time high. People are not looking for a fairy tale but for reality and hope. *Against Medical Advice* is a story of real-life adversity but bathed with hope.

If you're looking for a warm fuzzy book then *Against Medical Advice* is not it. This is book is raw and real. You will at times cheer and at other times cry as you read through the stories of life in Romania, the challenges of a new life in a new country, divorce, a serious and potentially debilitating stroke. This is a book of strength, willpower and grace. Simone shares more than her story but sends forth a message of hope, a message of potential, a message that you and I can survive and thrive even when life throws us those unexpected curve balls.

How do you grapple with having such a lifestyle of health, self-discipline and then to find yourself lying on a kitchen floor with your husband and young children looking at you wondering what happened? For many that would be an end, end of hope, end of a dream but for Simone is was a beginning of what it means to bounce back to push through. Simone's life is more than a story, it's a message. One we all need to slowly read and breathe in.

It is an honor to know Simone. I have come to appreciate her raw, real and vulnerable personality and I know you will share those same feelings as you meet her through these pages.

Dr. R. Irwin, PhD

Courage to live

Elegance. Open-minded. Dignity. Amazing leader.

I was participating in yet another Zoom seminar, and I was listening to her speaking. She was also a participant.

There were more people in this break-out room but she is the only one I remembered.

Although living in completely different time zones, we connected. It was December 2020.

I was already a published author, she had book ideas in her mind.

She told me I inspired her. I just shared what I knew about the publishing world.

I was inspired by her passion, her life experience, and how she has helped people with serious illnesses.

I believe in what she teaches because I've experienced it on my own before I even met her. In multiple ways. There are more people like Simone, like me, and probably like you, who are reading this. You're looking for an alternative way to heal yourself, and this is what you'll find in this book.

Modern medicine has saved many lives, and there's no question that they'll do everything they know to help other people. It's just that old truth that everything is not for everybody.

We have so many ways to travel from point A to point B. Planes, cars, trains, buses, bikes and motorbikes, hybrid cars, boats, and ferries. And yes, also on foot or by using horses, donkeys, etc. "the old fashion ways". Slow but steady.

But for some reason, when it comes to a healing journey, often only the "fast ones" are acceptable.

Simone's courage to speak with an open heart, stand for the things that matter to her, and be respectable to other choices, is much needed these days where we have so much fear around us.

This book is a warning but also a way out.

Much of the thinking-processes described in this book are familiar to me because I almost died four times before I decided to live fully, with all the courage I have.

When you're afraid to live, too scared to live fully, to face your fears, you'll be faced with death.

Like, someone's asking you – are you sure? Are you really sure living is scary enough?

Most people fight back.

And for most people, a near-death experience changes your life. Not for everybody but fortunately, this is not the case here.

She's a quick learner. Writing this book took a lot of courage. And it completed her healing.

I hope it'll help you too!

Birgit Itse

Writer, Author, Speaker

Introduction 💛

I always loved writing and dreamed of joining the much-coveted author club. Though the idea of writing on that level filled me with a warm, fuzzy feeling of excitement I didn't know what exactly I would write about. Sure, I could pull readers into my own world of fantasy and fairy tales but that was such a private world to me, one that I discovered when I started reading fairy tale stories as a child. That was a world I would escape to just so that I could have a respite from the bleak, harsh world of communism that was the focus of the society I lived in. No one was allowed in that world but me. I didn't want to share the magic of it with anyone.

So, I made a promise to myself that when the right story comes along, I will write it and share it with the world. I waited patiently for over two decades for the story to arrive.

On October 11, 2011 the story made a grand entrance into my life and changed me forever. The story, or as I refer to it, THE STORY, definitely surpassed my wildest dreams and expectations. I had always thought that one day I would write about the fairy tales of love in my life....my wedding....the magic of the moment when I called the man I married my husband....becoming a mom and how each time is different.....the inexplicable bond between mom and baby at birth.... but no, life had something else in store for me.

Though I grew up in a family that had to always push forward and overcome, I had to learn what pushing forward and overcoming was all about when done alone, with no safety net and with a life and death situation thrown in, for good measure. I share that with you here, in this book, in this story.

THE STORY opened the door of my destiny, helped me find my purpose and allowed me to finally step into myself and live life from purpose. It grew and evolved me far beyond what I thought was possible, beyond what happened, and it propelled me beyond where and who I was.

It showed me that life is not about OUTlook or OUTcomes or even about things working OUT but rather that an INcident is the catalyst to INdependence and that life is above all else an INside job.

In this book I take you through THE STORY. Come with me, let me show you....

"It always seems impossible until it's done."

Nelson Mandela

CHAPTER 1

Meeting Me

"*I'm strong, I can totally do this!*" So I say. I don't believe even one bit of it, but everybody else does.

"*Of COURSE, you can do it,*" says Ego, almost matter of fact.

"*Yes, yes you can Simone,*" adds Inner Me.

"*Look, think about it, everybody else has handled this. Thousands of people are divorced. There is absolutely no reason why YOU can't handle it. It's not like anyone died of divorce,*" continues Ego, exasperated that he has to state the obvious. I swear, if it wasn't for the impatience and exasperation, I would think that was God talking to me.

But Ego's right. Thousands of women get divorced and become single moms every year. Now I'm one of them, and if they can do it, I can do it. I try to push through with the thoughts, but I dissolve into tears.

"*Goddamn it Simone, stop being so damn soft!*" he says raising his voice.

These two have been with me, through and through. I am never without them. They are my trusted advisors. We're like the three musketeers.

Ego is the male side of me and my conscious mind. He's always playful, somewhat conceited, arrogant, alpha and a perfectionist who must always control all things, cause shit and have fun. Don't get me wrong, I love my Ego. Ego has never, not once, told me to play safe, to not take the leap of faith and to just stay in the comfort of familiarity. If anything, Ego has always pushed me out of my comfort zone and encouraged me to jump and do, or at least try. He has always known that anything is possible and that within me is an immense and infinite ability to create whatever I want without limitation. Without him I probably would never have survived many crises in my life, like the attempted abduction when I was seven years old.

Inner Me is the feminine side of me, my subconscious mind and part of infinite intelligence, soft and patient, a highly intuitive, beautiful feminine energy. She has full grasp of everything and functions at all levels. She is always calm, composed, compassionate and the epitome of kindness. She is the definition of pure LOVE who always gives unconditionally. She's all about feeling and doesn't ever use reasoning, rather she communicates with me via intuition, inspiration and impulses.

And then there's me – Outer Me – the one I see in the mirror, the one who's wounded, struggles, tries, and who hates complying with society's norms, most of which are senseless and limiting. Outer Me has been taught to rely on all things of the physical world that she can see, hear, smell, taste and touch. Outer Me is also the one who's usually in cahoots with Ego, loves to push the envelope and test limits.

 I got to know Inner Me and Ego on a bus, back when I was 19 and on my way to school. I've been speaking with them through thoughts and inner conversations regularly since that fateful meeting. That day, while on my way to school,

Inner Me must've felt compelled to see me in the flesh and introduce herself to me, so she pulled out of my body and watched me from above. I literally saw my body from above, completely detached from it. Ego, who would never let anyone one-up him, decided to do the same, so he joined Inner Me, watching her watch me and watching me watch him and her, all the while watching both of us. And thus, the three of us got acquainted. An extraordinary out-of-body, magical experience, called Astral Projection, that is as priceless to me as creating my children and birthing them into this world.

This experience wasn't so out of the ordinary for me, as I'd been getting lost in my own imagined magical worlds since I was very young anyway. And Freud talked about the Ego, Superego and Id before even my parents were born, so technically speaking all this was normal and quite common really, nothing but a trilogy of the self.

But if I was to ever tell anyone about this trilogy, that there are three of me, I'm sure they would think I'm 100% legitimately crazy. Spiritual awakening is something suspicious, weird and occult, something that happens only to the chosen ones, like you need to be hit by lightning to justify that kind of thinking if you're a normal person.

The only person I've ever taken time to justify anything to is myself, and of course to Inner Me and Ego. So, I believe I'm in good company. I trust them. Or at least I like to think that way.

Trust truly is the foundation of relationships, and my relationship with Inner Me and Ego is built on trust. I learned that lesson the hard way, when I lied to my dad about my whereabouts when I broke curfew. That sick feeling in the pit of my stomach was Inner Me trying to communicate, but I hadn't met her yet, so I had no idea. I ignored her. Like I ignored her many times to come.

"I refuse to act the way someone expects me to."

Madonna

CHAPTER 2

Going into Divorce

My divorce was the result of my fears from the past, events in the present and anxiety about the future.

Add tension to all that and everything falls apart. Everybody suffers, especially the children who are too young to understand the intricacies of relationships and what we bring with ourselves when we enter into them. This is exactly what's happening here – everyone is suffering. I'm in the middle of getting divorced and facing the looming new normal of my life. I'm stepping into unknown territory. Alone. Scared. Broken hearted.

Through the tears in my eyes I travel back to the day we met at work. Eleven years have passed but everything is fresh, like the first snow of the winter season.

Frank is the best-looking guy in that entire company. Hands down. I do so many double takes when I first lay eyes on him. The attraction is instant and soon thereafter we're inseparable. Working at the same company has many perks. We see each other throughout the day, eat lunch together, walk to our cars together and he helps me with whatever I need (or whatever I create to need help with just to see him).

Every morning he has coffee waiting for me on my desk and sometimes even something to eat. He sweeps me off my feet.

I like him so much that one night he even gets me out of my bath to go meet him at 10:00 pm. That's a cardinal sin in my books. It's always me that dictates when a meeting, get together or date happens with guys.

I know I like him. A LOT.

We marry five years later. Marcus, our first child, is our ring boy. If something can be done against the norm, it's how I want it done. I knew early on that I wanted to have kids young. Partly because I want to shatter another norm, the norm of thousands of years: have kids after you get married – in other words, *don't have kids out of wedlock*, and partly because I hate desperation and I didn't want to be a desperate 40-year-old with a loudly ticking biological clock. The maternal side of me couldn't care less about that stupid *don't have kids out of wedlock* rule, even if I tried really hard to care. If love is present and I want to have a baby, you can bet that I will have the baby. And then there's the norm du jour: establish your career first and have kids after. There was absolutely **no way** I would ever even consider the thought of having kids in my late thirties or early forties and run the risk of being fat, sick and tired afterward. I knew that the older you get the harder it is to lose weight. Not to mention the increased risk of birth defects, miscarriage and low birth weight. No thanks. So, babies first for me, so that both I and they can be healthy, and also so that I can bounce back quickly. Truth be told, I also didn't want to be 60 when my first child is 20 and face the possibility of never meeting my grandchildren, especially if my children choose to delay starting their own families. At that rate I'd be 80 when they're having their first, and there was absolutely no way I'd let that happen. So, shortly after my 25th birthday I become a first-time mom to Marcus, our first son. *"Have kids only after you're married"* rule broken. Mission accomplished.

In our fairy tale, Frank and I have two wonderful sons to be grateful for. We are a beautiful family. Three more of my dreams that have come true.

I can't say there are beasts in every beautiful marriage, but certainly there were some in ours. There comes a time to fight the beast in every fairy tale, and when the lack of trust becomes impossible for Frank and me to ignore, it's time to have The Conversation. This is never easy. It's hard to have it with people you date, but with the person you are married to and committed to building a life with, the difficulty is incalculable. But still, it's easier than continuing to live with the false hope that one day, you'll wake up and the sweetness of the honeymoon will have returned.

Fears from the past

During these emotionally difficult times that precede divorce, my health and healthy lifestyle are my safety net and my constant distraction. Physically, I look really good. And I feel really good. I have great energy. I'm not lethargic. I always wondered why people complain about having trouble getting through the day. Not once in my life did I ever question how I'd get through the day. Quite the opposite. I always pushed through. To do otherwise was foreign to me. Both my parents worked their entire lives. Now in their 70s, they're still working. The only time my mother was a stay-at-home mom is when she had me and Max, my baby brother. All other times she worked, and hard. So did my dad. Back in Romania, under the most brutal communist regime imported from the former USSR, my dad did things that most men were afraid to do. He always hustled to provide over and above. I can say without doubt that he was hands-down the biggest bad-ass in the entire country. To me he is the incarnation of the Romanian version of Zeus. He went on to beat the system at its own game and made his way to North America. On his own terms. On his own schedule, planned and strategized with absolute precision.

He often worked two or three jobs when we joined him in Vancouver, BC. I have fond memories of being awakened in the middle of night when he arrived home from his pizza delivery job, two large hot pizzas in hand so we could all eat. A far cry from waking up before dawn to stand in line to buy bread as was the case in communist Romania.

Neither of my parents ever took a day off and they pushed through everything that came their way to provide for me and Max. We were blessed with such amazing, hardworking parents who taught us life lessons that no prestigious school ever does.

They say that the apple doesn't fall far from the tree, so I push through too. I work, I work out and I take care of the kids and the house. I don't worry about the physical aspects of daily life at all, like who's going to help me with the groceries, because I'm actually happy to carry them myself. I know I can do it. It's like a little workout, and I love to work out.

I'm an excellent planner. Control over everything around me is my comfort zone. All my friends would tell you that I always offered to drive when we'd go out. I did it because that way I could leave when I wanted to, not when someone else wanted to.

I've always been very determined – when I want something, I get it. One way or another, I find a way to get it. It's always been that way. That's the silver lining of communism – it teaches you to accept no other outcome.

The reason why Chinese and Eastern bloc gymnasts are so successful is all thanks to the brutal training regime of the Communist culture – **do not lose**. Winning is **the only** possible outcome. Do **whatever it takes** to win. Accept no other outcome.

So in an effort to avoid facing the pain of the separation, I plan my days meticulously. I leave no time for boredom or having nothing to do, because having nothing to do means feeling the pain and facing it. Doing things keeps my attention away from the feelings of pain, fear and despair. If anything, doing these things evokes other emotions like fulfillment and achievement...squatting more weight, running a faster mile on a higher incline...small achievements. All pertaining to my body.

I try to keep myself extremely busy and distracted, just so that I can avoid coming face to face with the excruciating pain of losing my marriage. Little did I know during those painful times of separation that facing my fears head on was the antidote to the fear itself.

I went into my marriage with big issues. I had the wrong attitude and the wrong thoughts. And whatever those thoughts consisted of is exactly what I manifested.

*"Never, ever let a man control you. Do you understand Simone? Always and I mean **always** have the upper hand. Do you get it?"*

"Do not ever let a man tell you what to do. Do not ever allow a man to control you!!! Financially or otherwise." I would look myself in the eye, in the mirror in my room when I was still living at home, and have those stern conversations with myself. On a regular basis, just to remind myself. I was literally programming myself.

I remember the words I said to myself on my wedding day, when I intentionally locked myself in the bathroom to have that conversation with myself before I say "I do" - a reminder of the promise I had made: *"Do you remember your promise? Do **not** go back on your word, Simone!"*

What I didn't know at that point is that you can have your self-worth and dignity even when you don't get the last word, even when you show your vulnerability and your weaknesses.

I have been working since I was 14, because it has been my choice. I wanted to have my own money so I'd always have something to fall back on. Even when I asked my parents for money to go out with my friends, I always kept the money I had made as a backup. If they didn't give me money, I still had my own. I secured myself.

And throughout the separation process, I am so glad I had developed those habits of self-sufficiency. I'd been so right about going to work because now I can provide, I am not dependent. That's always been one of my greatest fears – being dependent on someone and then having nothing to fall back on.

Events in the present

Inside myself, I'm falling apart. Emotionally, I'm in pieces. Totally broken. I put on a brave face and lie to the world every day, making everyone believe that all is great and I'm doing fantastic.

Onward I push, shoving the pain deeper and deeper, so that it doesn't have a chance of coming to the surface. At the top of my to-dos are kids, gym and meal planning, to support the desired outcomes from the gym.

It's been six months and I still try very hard every single day to keep the overwhelming feelings of the separation and divorce process at bay. It's so incredibly tough for so many reasons. We need to redesign our relationship as parents instead of as husband and wife, and that tension between us needs to be eliminated and left behind. New boundaries need to be set, but first, I need to work out my personal boundaries as well. And how to articulate them. We're still parents and our children need both of us. So it's up to us to work it out, to be adults, to take responsibility for our choices, good and bad. The only problem is that every time I see him, the feelings of pain, with anger in tow, come to the surface with lava-like power, as if erupting from a volcano.

Although I know it's for the greater good in the end, for myself and for the kids, my heart breaks every time I see the sadness in them. It's so obvious. Written all over their faces and deep in their eyes. "When's dad coming? I miss him." are words I hear daily.

It's hard for me to answer those questions, but I don't blame them. It's just that I don't know how to answer them. It's not like I have a divorce manual that contains all possible questions I could be asked, nor have I done this before, like a practice run so I can be prepared for conversations with the kids.

I try to explain, and to be calm and patient, swallowing my own pain and sadness, but it's as tough on me as it is on them.

Divorce is difficult...the sadness, constant questions, uncertainty. I'm doing my best. Trying so hard to keep my pain, hurt, fear, anger, disappointment, guilt, anxiety, frustration and self-blame to myself and away from them is mentally and emotionally exhausting. This, after lying to the rest of the world about it all on a daily basis. Lies are heavy to carry. They weigh tons on the heart and on the soul. The pain and hurt are like a wound on my soul that just won't heal. The fear is a three-headed demon that claws at the wound on my soul. The anger is what pokes it, while the disappointment, guilt, anxiety, frustration and self-blame are the fuel it uses to stay alive.

I single-handedly feed this demon that torments me. Outside, I'm calm. Because I'm really doing it. I'm getting divorced. So I say to my little boy, "Not today baby. He'll be here in a few days. You could call him if you want."

Distraction is the name of the game. Denial too. I do not accept that my marriage is actually coming to an end. In the deep corners of my heart I think this is just a bad dream I'm going to eventually wake up from, so in the meantime I push my pain down and just do things I enjoy, like going to the gym, riding my motorcycle and having some fun until everything goes back to normal. I have no interest in coming face to face with the reality of this. Divorce has always been one of my biggest fears. Divorce = failure. And I **hate** to fail.

At anything. To me a failed marriage is in essence failing life.

At a conscious level, I'm still actually completely unaware of my determination and my ability to create and manifest everything in my life – the good and the bad. I really am very true to my word. All my thoughts lead me to decisions that go on to become what I experience in my life.

I just don't know it. Yet. I'm oblivious to how I'm creating my future with my own thoughts. With a lot of energy, as usual. As a mother, everything was the kids and doing things with them, like going to the park. As Simone, everything was the gym. All leftover energy and focus were poured into planning meals that contained what I needed to support the workouts, and into the workouts themselves. And they were serious business. I would regularly squat or deadlift to the point of throwing up in the women's change room, where I'd be asked if I was pregnant. To do less than that was disappointing. I look like a million bucks. I love the looks and stares I get in the change room. I'm asked to do fitness competitions on a regular basis and personal trainers in the gym tell me that their clients want to achieve "her ass" or say "I want her arms". My 20-something-year-old self doesn't hold a candle to my 30-something-year-old self.

Anxiety about the future

"I don't know how to do this," I say out loud, feeling tears well up in my eyes.

"Seriously, how am I going to do this? Something bad is probably going to eventually happen! Something's going to happen to me! Everything in my life is shit!!"

Ego and Inner Me are silent. *"I mean, now I'm responsible for the bills and for the kids all by myself,"* I continue.

Silence from both.

The fear is strong and relentless. The demon is not the timid, weak "I hope nothing happens" type. It's more like "Oh my dear God! How am I going to do this all by myself? With two kids!" type. Ferocious and ever present.

It's stress on top of stress. I'm stressed about how I'm going to pay the mortgage for the huge house we bought together. Our dream house. And on top of that, I'm scared to be alone. And all this is on top of the pain and anger that I still push down hard every single day.

*"Guys, I have **never** been alone. I'm actually scared to live alone. I have never lived on my own. You guys know this. What if somebody breaks in and kills me and the kids?"* I ask, feeling the knot in my throat, my heart starting to race. **That** is the physical manifestation of stress...feeling stress physically!

"None of that will happen," offers Inner Me. *"You are always protected."*

"Really? Will whoever is protecting me pay the mortgage too?" I snap back, as tears roll down my cheeks, taking my black mascara with them.

"I've been telling you to keep a few metal baseball bats around the house," says Ego.

Six months alone in this house. Separated but not yet divorced. In limbo. A single but still married woman en route to a new life. Alone. About to collide with a wrecking ball.

This is definitely not something I wanted my life to be and it's definitely not what I envisioned for myself, in my wildest dreams.

So many fears. Too many.

Fear is believing in negative things. It's the belief that something dangerous or bad is going to happen. The subconscious mind doesn't know what's good or bad and what's real and what's make-believe. You decide that with your conscious mind and give energy to it. And your subconscious says: *"Okay, whatever you want. I'm right on it. I'll bring whatever you give energy to with your thoughts into physical reality."*

The fear causes conflict within me, because, in reality, what could actually happen to me? I push away my anxiety with the affirmations that I'm 35, I live in my own house, I have two wonderful children and I have no warnings health-wise. My blood test results are exemplary. I invest so much into my health that I feel I'm completely untouchable. I'm young. I'm literally doing absolutely everything that's recommended to stay healthy. My diet supports the building of the muscles I want, stamina for running and my strength for the tough two-hour workouts I put myself through six to seven times a week. Stress to me is part of life and everyone goes through it, so it's no big deal.

My mindset – not my mental health, but my thinking – is very sick, negative and very broken. I've been living with an increasing feeling of doom, which manifests physically nine days before my 36th birthday. I was expecting the house to get broken into, or my car to be stolen, or the house to be flooded and we'd lose all our belongings. The fact that this "something is about to happen" refers to my health comes as an absolute shock. So shocking that it defies belief.

The night before doomsday is no different than any other night in any way, except I know I have a party coming up. A big Thanksgiving and birthday party. Canadian Thanksgiving and my birthday are mere days apart so why not celebrate them both? I am so excited. About 20 people have said yes. I feel so good. I can hardly wait. It's been a very long time since I've celebrated anything; my days, weeks and months have been monotonous and similar – my routine full of the same old, same old. And since my relationship with Frank has become civil, we could celebrate that too. The pain and anger are still very much alive and well deep – very deep – within me.

The garage door opening distracts me from the work I'm doing on my computer in the kitchen. That could only be Frank. No one else has the automatic garage door opener.

Bella jumps from her bed and rushes to the back door that leads to the garage, wagging her tail in excitement.

He walks into the kitchen, Bella following loyally behind him.

"Hi Simone, how are you?" he says very formally.

"Oh, hi Frank. I'm good," I lie. "How are you?"

"Good. How are the kids? Did you guys eat?"

"Yeah, we did. They're upstairs, go ahead and see them if you want."

Frank still works close to our house so he stops by whenever he wants to see the kids. The boys are always ecstatic to see him. I'm surprised he stopped by tonight, since he's coming to the party tomorrow too and he'd see the boys then. But we agreed that we would put our children first, and not abide by any of the timed bullshit the courts suggest, like "You can have them until 5:00 pm on Friday. Make sure you have them back by 5:00 pm." I can't fathom using the clock to time visits between parents and children. It's a huge blessing that Frank and I agree on being liberal with access to our kids, so he's welcome to see them any time. Besides, I know seeing their dad will make the boys' day, and since I would give them the world, how could I ever stand in the way of Frank coming to see them?

He goes upstairs. Their shrieks of happiness both kill me a little and fill me with endless joy.

"Sometimes life is going to hit you in the head with a brick. Don't lose faith."

Steve Jobs

CHAPTER 3

Meet the Monster ♡

Today is the big day. I open my eyes. It's Saturday, the 8th of October, 2011. There are so many things that flood my mind as I think about today's to-do list. In chronological order of course. Breakfast, gym, shopping for wine and last-minute things, cleaning, shower, setting the table and getting ready. Then my thoughts settle on particular details about the leg workout, and about how I should juggle the time since I want to take the motorcycle to go to the gym and the car for the shopping.

I haven't told anyone that this Thanksgiving dinner is also my 36th birthday celebration. Not many people know that I only have nine more days of being 35. This get-together is not about me, it's about giving thanks for friendships, which I have relied on heavily during this emotionally difficult time. I'm sure I kept Starbucks in business with all the coffees I had with friends to commiserate and discuss how to improve our workouts.

It's 7:00 am. No time to snooze the alarm today, so I get out of bed and go to the bathroom. *"Ugh, what a shitty day to have a headache!"* I think as I plop myself on the toilet, head in my hands. *"Maybe the shower will make me feel better."* It doesn't.

I've had headaches before. Not often but sometimes, usually caused by precipitation. I guess everybody has them once in a while. My work is mainly sitting in front of a computer, even during meetings, so I attribute my headaches to looking at a screen for 8 hours a day in an office that doesn't offer fresh air, my "computer neck" posture and the tension in my shoulders and neck. I don't worry much, since one or two Advils always do the job. And a massage. This time it feels different, though. Slightly. But I don't pay attention to it.

I look outside. It's dry but cloudy. Clouds are typical of October. I rejoice at the dry pavement.

"Maybe it's going to rain," I think as I pick up my phone to check the weather. No rain expected.

So it isn't the weather that's causing this weird headache. Anyway, it is what it is. I don't have time to decipher what's causing the headache. More important things await.

"Great! I can ride!" I rejoice again, shifting my thoughts to what I should wear to the gym. Thoughts of excitement for the night to come swirl in my head as I get dressed. It's definitely going to be an amazing night and I can't wait to taste everything that the guests bring over.

I head to the kitchen.

I need to eat so I can get to the gym as soon as possible. Gym is always a **must**. There are no days off. It's **very** seldom that I take a day off to "rest", and even then, my way of resting is doing some sort of cardio or other calorie-burning activity. Today is going to be no different.

My traditional fuel for the leg day destruction is pancakes made with protein powder and frozen fruit, slathered with a layer of peanut butter, a layer of Greek yogurt, a generous drizzle of honey and a sprinkle of cinnamon. I always look forward to it more than any other workout. Leg day is always Saturday, when there's no rush and I've had a chance to sleep in a little. In fact, in my world, Saturday is International Leg Day. The pancakes are so delicious that I almost feel guilty for having them. Getting fat is another one of my greatest fears. Not getting sick...getting fat.

This is all strategized. Leg muscles are the biggest muscle group in the body, and to grow they need to be nourished and fed with the nutrients necessary for growth and health.

Breakfast consists of good quality calories that I bulldoze through at the gym, and immediately post workout I have more protein with some sort of clean, natural sugar, and then a nice meal afterwards. The blueprint to muscle growth. Tonight's meal at 7 pm would be the epic Thanksgiving/birthday meal that my muscles will thank me for by growing.

Breakfast first. While we were happily married, Frank always made coffee since he was the first one up and out of bed. I don't even notice that the coffee is made. I pour myself a cup as I always did when we lived together, and start getting out the ingredients for the pancakes. *"Ugh, today is such a terrible day to have a headache,"* I think to myself again. I grab the bottle of Advil liquid-gel pills from the cupboard and toss two in my mouth, washing them down with coffee.

"The workout will help," I tell myself. Today is a big day.

I notice little Bella outside in the backyard chasing whatever bugs are still around in the fall. The boys are in the garage, helping their dad bring in the folding chairs. Frank arrived early. I had asked for his help with the party and if Frank ever has the chance to help someone, he'll jump to do it. It's one of the things I always loved about him.

Marcus walks into the kitchen with two chairs and sets them against the wall by the sliding doors that lead to the backyard. "Hi mom," he says and walks over to give me a kiss. Then he's out again.

I'm left to myself in the kitchen to get on with things.

I take out most of the ingredients for pancakes and set them on the counter. The coffee-maker lets out some steam.

All of a sudden, lightning strikes inside my head. The blinding white light takes over my entire internal field of vision and engulfs the inside of my skull. I'm blinded. The light gets brighter and more intense than a spotlight. I'm stunned. Unable to move. It seems like eternity, but in actuality it happens in a mere nanosecond. I'm whisked off to a world that opens just for me. Time freezes. All things I know disappear and the most beautiful silence reigns supreme. Distantly, in the deep corners of myself, I know – in fact, it's more of a feeling than a knowing, or maybe it's both – that the world I've known as home for the last 35 years and 356 days is actually not home. This world to which I was whisked away, this is home. It's peaceful. It's light. It's serene. It's inviting. I float away in its vastness and purity, feeling like I'm a piece of it. A fiber of a never-ending piece of fabric that I can only call love. Complete and unconditional love. It's this fabric that eternity is made of. God's presence is obvious. God is the tailor that uses this fabric to perpetually construct the eternal Universe.

I love floating in that world that is home...I love feeling so light...I love the peace...I love the love...I love the eternal serenity. But before I can even orient myself to what is going on, I'm yanked out of the ultrabright white world of love, out of the serenity and the sounds of silence, out of the frozen time, and transported right back to my kitchen. All things are waiting for me exactly as I had left them.

I blink my eyes, momentarily disoriented and confused. Thoughts shoot across my mind at warp speed, colliding into each other. What world was that? What world is this? Why was that world so much better than this one? Why am I here? Why can't I stay there? What do I have to do here?

When can I go back there? Can I go there at will? What was the purpose of my trip there? How long was that trip?

No answers. I notice that I'm on the floor. That's confusing. What am I doing here? Bella is still happily chasing bugs in the backyard. That's cute. Marcus, Roman and Frank are all in the kitchen and looking at me, concern and confusion written all over their faces. That's weird.

The beautiful silence is gone. The sounds of this world are grotesque, nothing peaceful and inviting about them. The headache is still present. Stronger than ever. Is this what's been produced in hell and inserted into my head? The pain is almost unbearable. Is this pain the price to pay for visiting that world? The pressure is of such intensity, I'm afraid that my head will explode like an overinflated balloon.

No. This is not a headache. I don't even know what to name it. It's like an animal inside my head, like the Tasmanian devil. A monster. *"I have no idea who you are but you are indescribable."* I've experienced incredible physical pain, but this...this is something of another world, another universe, another dimension. It can perhaps be compared to the pain of childbirth and passing kidney stones at the same time. I've done the former, not the latter, but I've heard it's more painful than giving birth to twins.

"Maybe I brought it with me from that world," I think.

I look around to ensure that I am indeed back to my familiar world. Yes, I am. I'm on my kitchen floor.

"Did they see me fall?" I wonder. *"I don't think they did. Did they discover me?"*

Well, obviously, as they weren't here when the lightning struck, but they're here now.

"How long have I been lying here?"

AGAINST MEDICAL ADVICE

Silence. Ego and Inner Me don't know much about counting time. I could have been on the floor for 30 seconds...a full five minutes...half an hour. Who knows?

The question of how long this time-travel experience lasted is somehow irrelevant.

What catches my attention is my amazing Marcus looking at me. The worry is written all over his young, angelic face. His big blue eyes are studying me intently, looking for an answer. He says something to me in a language that I intuitively know is not of this world. Am I in a parallel universe where things and people are made to look like they're from my universe and my world, except they speak another language?

Or have I left my ability to understand English back in the world I was transported to, the world where I had a beautiful meeting with what I could only perceive as God? I mean, who else has the power to stop time like that? The eternity of the time I was there was all so grand and interminable. Everything was commanded to stand still just for me, so that I can take it all in, absorb it, feel it and try to understand it, which of course was impossible. An experience like that is not something the human mind can make sense of or understand.

The overwhelming feeling of peace I felt in that eternal moment is still imprinted on my very being. I was somewhat sad to leave behind that peaceful, serene divinity shrouded in white light, but that sadness was quickly replaced by the powerful inexplicable love for Marcus and Roman as soon as I rejoined them back in this world. Clearly my work was not done in this world just yet.

I question whether all this is an illusion. Am I stuck in a dream? I lift my arm and look at it to see if my body is recognizable to me. I see my pink nails, courtesy of my favorite Essie nail polish that the nail technician has waiting for me when I go for my manicure.

My Tiffany bracelets are on my wrist. I recognize them and recall which one I got for my birthday, which one I got for Christmas and which one was a Mother's Day gift.

This recognition brings me relief. Confused, I reach out and touch Marcus to see if he is real. He takes my hand and says something else to me that is just as incomprehensible as the first thing I heard him say. He then turns his head to his dad, who is now crouching down looking at me with both worry and curiosity. He says something that is in a language just as bizarre as the one Marcus spoke seconds earlier.

Does my family speak a language I don't? I try to reach deep in my memory bank to see if there's any trace of a memory of this fact. My head hurts so incredibly bad that this feat is impossible. I give up.

Momentarily, the monster headache moves to the forefront of my attention, as if to say *"You need to deal with me NOW."*

I push myself up off the floor slowly and open the cupboard again to get more Advil. For a split second I consider taking the whole bottle, thinking, *"One or two won't get rid of this kind of headache."* But I only tip two pills into my trembling hand.

Turning around to get something to wash the pills down, I nearly bump into Frank, who's standing there ready with a glass of water.

Even though we're officially separated, here he is, still doing things for me. I swallow the pills with a gulp.

"...now?" he asks.

I move my attention from the headache to the fact that he's speaking English again. *"This is great. All is okay and I probably just imagined this whole thing with the white light in my head. I just have a really bad headache, that's all,"* I reach for Inner Me and Ego again.

Inner Me is awfully silent. Maybe the lightning inside my head killed her.

"Oh God, no," I think. I reach out for her again.

"It's just a really bad headache, right?"

Silence.

"...to me," says my husband. He is still my husband.

I turn my attention back to him. "Huh?"

"Talk to me, Simone," he says.

I understand everything he says. **Everything**. The whole sentence.

I turn to Marcus. I want him to say something; I want to see if he speaks English or whether he'll continue using that language that's foreign to me.

"Mom, what's wrong? Are you ok?" he asks. The concern is carved into his voice and worry written all over his face. He's only ten but within the last year he's grown up too fast. The last thing he needs is another drama. The physical separation is enough. I turn back to look at Frank. "Simone, please say something. Are you ok?"

Roman is only five. He, too, is looking up at me, waiting for an answer.

"Umm, I have a headache," is all I can muster, summoning all my energy, strength and power.

Frank sighs audibly with relief.

"Come sit down," he says as he puts his hand on my lower back and guides me to the couch in the living room.

Walking there takes another huge chunk of my energy. I am very shaken.

I sit down and rest my head in my hands. As my head drops the headache intensifies.

I let out a groan and straighten myself to bring my head back up.

The pain subsides ever so slightly. Frank and the kids are right there with me.

"Lie down, mom," says Marcus. "You'll feel better." He places a pillow by the armrest and picks up the plush throw and wraps it around me. This kid is well beyond his years.

I shake my head gently, afraid that too much movement will intensify the pain. It does. A thousand-fold.

"Here, have some coffee." Frank hands me my mug that he filled to the rim. Black, no sugar. Just the way I like it. I take a sip, breathing in the aroma, momentarily enjoying the pleasure.

"Do you want something to eat?" he asks. "Maybe some toast?"

"Sure," I say quietly, almost whispering. The vibration of my very words reverberates in my head, amplifying the headache or whatever this pain is.

I get up slowly and walk back to the kitchen, where Frank is placing two slices of my favorite bread in the toaster. The jar of almond butter is already on the counter. He always knew what I liked.

I turn back to searching for Inner Me. I'm really worried that the lightning strike inside my head killed her and I'll never have her to consult with again. Inner Me has always been so wise and so right. Her advice has never let me down and she has never lied to me. Ego, the master of my obedient mind, has led me astray more times than I can count.

I look at the clock on the stove, the green light showing 10:22. Oh, it's getting so late. I need to get to the gym as soon as possible. Maybe I'll do a quick but intense workout so I can get everything done for the party.

"Not a good idea," Inner Me chimes in.

She's alive. And well. My heart skips a beat of happiness that she's back.

"Why not?" I ask her.

"You're not well. You need to see a doctor. You should also cancel the party," she tells me, gentle as always.

"Absolutely not!" I reply sharply. How dare she even suggest such a thing? The gym is my **life**. I don't take days off. Her suggestion is ridiculous and ludicrous. It's not like I'm heading to the bar. I don't even let her reply.

I take my last bite of toast. I feel better now that I have some food and coffee in me. But this headache is relentless. I grab the bottle of Advil, pop two more pills in my mouth and wash them down with the last bit of coffee.

At the Gym

I slowly make my way upstairs to change for the gym. Frank follows me.

"Are you feeling better?" he asks.

"Yeah, a bit. Thank you so much for making me breakfast." Things are clearly awkward. We're separated and I'm still hurt, but at that moment I want to walk over and give him a hug. "And for the coffee," I add.

"No problem. But are you ok? What happened there?"

"I really don't know. It's just a really really bad headache." I actually want to tell him all about the lightning and the fact that time stood still and that for a few minutes there he and our son were speaking a language I didn't understand. I decide against it. He wouldn't understand. He'll think I'm crazy. Besides, I can't make any sense of this myself.

"Let's do this," I say out loud, talking to myself.

"Do what?" he asks.

"Oh sorry, I was just thinking out loud. I'm heading to the gym."

"Now?" He's surprised.

"Yes, of course now."

I walk over to the closet, grab a pair of pants and a Lululemon top and make my way into the bathroom to change.

Changing takes a huge amount of energy. *"So weird,"* I think to myself.

I go back downstairs and bend over to pick up my running shoes to put them on. As soon as my head is not in the upright position, the sharp pain attacks me again with no mercy. The pain is concentrated in my left temple and towards my eye. The level of pain is indescribable to myself, much less to someone else. To call this a migraine would be an insult to the pain. *"They really need to have a word that truly captures what I feel now,"* I think.

I grab my jacket from the closet and put it on slowly, then head out to the garage, motorcycle key in hand.

I love riding the Green Monster, as I call it. It's my second. I bought this beauty last year as my marriage was crumbling.

The streets are dry and the air is rather warm – about 13-14 degrees Celsius, 55-57 Fahrenheit . It's doable. Over the last little while I had become a motorcycle riding snob. While some people ride well into December as long as the pavement is dry, I only ride when the temperature is at least

15 degrees Celsius. I had paid my dues riding in cold weather. Not anymore. It's all about my comfort now and I hate getting crap in the motorcycle chain. Especially salt because it makes it rust. I grab the handlebars to straighten out the front so I can roll the motorcycle out onto the street to start it. I've never understood why people start their motorcycles in their garage; toxic exhaust fumes would linger in the garage and make their way into the house.

I try to push the bike upright so I can take the kickstand off but can't seem to make it happen. I try again, to no avail. Even though the bike weighs 400 lbs. and I only weigh 120, I've never had a problem with this before.

My head is pounding by now. The monster headache is trying to get out through my left temple. I don't understand it. Advil usually takes care of pain quickly. By now, I've had four Advil pills in an hour and no relief.

"Could you please take my bike out?" I ask my husband, who's gone back to carrying things from his car into the house.

Without saying a word, he walks over, grabs the handlebars, straightens out the front and walks the bike out and starts it.

"Thank you so much," I say in a very formal tone as he walks back into the garage. I try to make eye contact, but he doesn't even look in my direction. "No prob," he mutters back, clearly upset that I'm leaving.

"Mom, where are you going?" asks Marcus as he walks into the garage.

Roman, close behind him, runs over to me and wraps his arms around my hips. "Mommyyyyy...," he says in his angelic little voice. "Don't gooooooo."

"Mom's going to the gym, baby," I say as I bend down and kiss his cheek. He knows the gym; I've taken him to the daycare there on countless occasions. A dagger stabs my left temple – or at least that's what it feels like. The pain is excruciating. I let out a moan of pain.

"Are you sure, mom? Are you ok?" asks Marcus.

"I'm fine, baby," I lie, forcing a fake smile.

"I love you boys," I say to both kids and kiss Marcus on the cheek.

I grab my helmet from the shelf and as I start putting it on my head, I understand why motorcycle helmets and headaches don't mix well. Helmets are made to fit snugly in the area of the head that a baseball cap covers. The snug fit should not be squeezing the head, nor should it be painful. Today, it's beyond the definition of a level 10 kind of pain.

The helmet is actually more of a vise right now. I push past the pain, flip the visor down, mount up and roar off down the street.

The gym is my second home. It's where my iron gets sharpened, so to speak. It's where I've pushed my mind and body past their limits. It's both my private hell and divine heaven – depending on the day. Today is clearly going to be a visit to hell's deepest and darkest spot. My headache is intensifying by the minute.

Inner Me had pleaded with me to take the day off from the gym right after the staggering lightning strike this morning.

 Seems like she doesn't know me at all. Even after all these years. The gym is oxygen for me. How can she even **think** of such a thing, much less actually present it to me as a suggestion I would even consider?

In the gym, as my monster headache rages on inside my head, oblivious to everyone around me, I make my way straight to the leg press. Next to the squat rack, the leg press is my all-time favorite machine. It's really a reverse squat if you ask me. It takes all my leg and glute muscles to the highest point of pain and beyond, making them beg for mercy. The secret to muscular strength, power and size is all in pushing muscles past their limit. I do that every single time I train legs. In my opinion, it's almost a waste of time to train unless you push past your limit of pain. This is why the headache doesn't hold me back from the gym today.

I try to load the machine with the usual two 45-pound plates - one each side - to warm up, but I can feel my limbs trembling. I can't even lift one of the plates. But I refuse to look weak or broken to my fellow gym addicts.

"I'm just going to warm up without weight," I tell myself, giving up the idea of my usual warm up set.

Angry music is blaring in my ears, trying to drown out Inner Me's pleas, the monster that's still thrashing around inside my head, and getting me pumped up for the leg annihilation that's about to take place.

I get myself adjusted on the machine, place my feet on the footplate and engage my core. I unlock the weight stopper. The weight comes down with such force that it nearly breaks both my legs. Without the leg strength I've developed over the last 20 years, I am 100% sure that my knees would've snapped in that moment. Summoning every ounce of strength I could muster I push the weight back up and lock the footplate – I had to, I would've rather died than have anyone in that gym believe that I couldn't lift that measly 40-pound footplate that's part of the machine. My usual weight for this exercise is 450 pounds.

The way I look at it is that pain is temporary. The pain of labor and birth of two big boys was beyond what the mind can even conceive, but it passed, and I survived, so pain doesn't intimidate me. After labor and birth, I thought, anything would be a walk in the park. Right now, I'm more inclined to think that the labor and birth were a walk in the park compared to the monster headache that's having its way with me.

After I push the weight up to the first notch and lock it, heaving, I struggle to catch my breath. That's the hardest physical thing I ever had to do. My muscles refuse to have any of it. I am in utter shock. My muscles loved giving me everything I asked of them, each and every time. We had an amazing relationship. What's going on here?

"I told you to take today off. What happened this morning was very serious. You are not okay right now." She is powerful. And relentless. She was able to drown out the loud, angry music. Here she goes again. She's quite annoying right now. The monster headache and Inner Me are in cahoots, against me.

I am jittery and my whole body is trembling.

Inner Me tries to take over. *"Ok, here's what we're going to do. Call Frank and ask him to come pick you up. Go home, call everyone, cancel the party and lie down. You need to rest. It's imperative."*

Is she kidding? Even though this headache is out to kill me, I'm still lucid enough to know that I **cannot** have my husband come and pick me up because I would have to leave the motorcycle here at the gym and I will do no such thing. Or we'd have to swap, with him riding the motorcycle back while I drove home in the car.

Oh, hell no. I refuse to be so weak that I have to ask someone to help me, much less my soon to be ex-husband. I am no weak woman, no damsel in distress in need of a man's help. To do any of what Inner Me was suggesting would mean betraying myself and breaking my promise to myself. I vowed to never depend on a man in any capacity, to never be at the mercy of a man, and to never let a man have power over me.

To call my husband asking for help at this crucial time, when we're separated, implies that I depend on him and need his help. I refuse to put myself in this position. I wish

Inner Me would quit pushing me to do this. She clearly must think I'm a weak, vulnerable girl. I'm not.

Because of this headache, it feels like I can't function properly.

"You know that headaches are related to the brain, right?" asks Inner Me.

"I know, I'll have to look into this whole thing," I tell her. *"But right now it's not a good time. I'll do it next week. I need to get the Thanksgiving party over and done with. This is Thanksgiving weekend, remember?"*

"But it's a long weekend. Today is Saturday. And Monday is also a holiday," she responds, gentle as she has always been.

"I really don't have time for it right now. I'm having the party. I'm not negotiating," I tell her sternly. *"The only way this party is getting canceled is if I die or the house catches on fire,"* I add, so she knows I'm serious about the party.

After all, it's just a headache. Okay, a **really horrible** headache. Everyone has off days like this every once in a while. I don't know why she's making such a big deal about a headache.

I get off the leg press machine and walk over to the weight rack.

"I'll do some arms instead," I think. Arms are always my easiest workout. Small muscles don't take as much energy as large muscles.

"It doesn't matter, Simone," Inner Me chimes in, as if I asked her opinion on it. *"You're feeling weak. You shouldn't be working out."*

I let out a laugh. I'm tempted to remind her that it's just a headache and a bad day at the gym, but I have no patience for her antics anymore, so I ignore her.

I pick up a 20-pound dumbbell to do some bicep curls and I nearly drop it. Luckily, I'm close enough to the rack that I drop it back on its spot. The left side of my body seems particularly weak. I realize that the arm is tingly.

Each time there's exertion, the monster in my head starts to thrash around, all to torment me. It tears through my brain and rips apart my blood vessels. The pain is like daggers that have sat in the hottest fires of hell, now jammed into my skull and turned. Slowly. By the Devil himself.

I refuse to accept defeat. I walk over to the "girly weights" as I call them and pick up a 5-pound dumbbell. Nope. The monster in my head makes me pay for that too. Obliterating pain arises. Defeated, I place the dumbbell back and start making my way back to the women's change room to grab my helmet and bag.

"Yay, you're leaving," says Inner Me. *"I'm so happy. You really aren't okay. You need to rest."* She's so great. She never holds grudges and she is **always** kind and compassionate.

Little does she know that I'm actually going because I want to get rid of this headache so I can have a good workout, not because she's been pleading with me. I'll be back here as soon as the headache is gone.

I'm shaking. I blame the coffee. And the monster inside my head. And maybe the Advils have something to do with it too. Although it doesn't make sense because they don't seem to work. At all.

I put the vise back on my throbbing head, slowly get on the motorcycle and make my way back home.

I have no recollection of how I made it to the gym and back home operating the motorcycle, processing information related to the traffic around me and balancing 400 lbs. of metal with legs that couldn't even press 40 pounds at the gym. But somehow, I do it. Probably because I gave myself no other choice. That's the beauty of having no choice – we always build one. I am reminded that my body is able to do extraordinary things.

The party

Back home I get into cleaning mode. Frank has done quite a bit of work. The huge bird is in the oven already and the table has been extended to accommodate all the people that are expected tonight.

I refuse to dedicate any thought to canceling the party. It's Saturday. People have made plans. They've cooked and organized things to bring over and they're prepared for it. How would I call and cancel all this because of a headache? I can't disappoint my friends.

I take two more Advil with the hope of sedating even an iota of the monster headache that continues to torture me. Maybe it's a certain number of pills that will do the trick and I just haven't taken enough to meet that threshold yet. The monotony of the vacuum cleaner puts me in a trance-like state. Thoughts flow freely in, out and around my mind.

"What should I wear?" I wonder. I already know it'll be a dress. I absolutely love to dress up. And I'm talking the whole nine yards – hair, makeup, killer outfit and sky-high heels. Anything less would be half-assing it. When the feminine side of me comes out, she comes all out.

"You should cancel the party," Inner Me interrupts. She has such bad timing and despite her good intentions, she sometimes rains on my parade. But she's always been right.

"No chance," I respond. *"I can't let people down. They committed to coming, I can't disappoint them."*

"But you're really not well," she insists gently.

"I'm totally fine, except for a headache. Everyone gets headaches," I tell her. *"Besides, I can't wait to see everyone and to celebrate."*

In one way it was good that I didn't know it was a stroke. I probably would have been like *"Oh my God, I had a stroke. **A fucking stroke!!!!** Strokes can **kill** people, dammit. If you're lucky you'll manage on your own while in a wheelchair, but too many cases are way more serious and leave you dependent on others to feed and clean you. Do you want that?"*

Worst case scenarios scare the shit out of me, in fact they paralyze me with fear.

Right now, it's just a headache. So I'm good enough to do whatever I need to do.

"We've got this," announces Ego. *"Suck it up and don't complain."*

"But it's so much," reminds Inner Me.

"No, it's not. Don't complain," Ego snaps at Inner Me.

He then turns to me. *"You're so strong. You've got this. You can do it. Suck it up. Don't look weak to people. You do not want people to look at you as a weakling."*

I love his words. They are so empowering.

I gather my strength, put the vacuum away and make my way upstairs and into the walk-in closet.

"Red," I think, and my favorite fitted dress comes to mind as I push hangers out of the way to get to it. *"And I'll match it with the Chanel lipstick."*

It's occasions like this that justify my sometimes-extravagant purchases. I did not need a $50 lipstick, but it's such a great shade that looks amazing with my skin tone, so why not?

"Oh, or white. I look awesome in white," I think, as I come across my favorite white dress. It's fitted, too. I think of all the compliments I get when I wear white. White is very unforgiving – it shows every flaw. But since I dedicate endless hours at the gym and my body looks amazing, I can pull off white, no problem.

"And it's after Labor Day," I continue. *"You shouldn't wear white after Labor Day,"* I think, reciting the rule in my head. *"Perfect!!! I'm wearing white,"* I decide, taking the dress off the hanger and holding it against myself as I look in the full-length mirror. If there's a rule, I want to be there to break it. Here's a rule and here I am, doing my duty of breaking it.

"Oooohhhhh or this one," I say to myself happily, picking up a fuchsia dress that I haven't yet worn. I hold that one against myself now. I love how feminine this color is.

"But the red one is more low-cut," I think. *"Hmmmm, be ultra-feminine in pink, break the stupid Labor Day rule, or make Frank see what he no longer has?"*

I grab the red dress, and lay it flat on the bed, then head back to the closet for my 5-inch heels.

"I need some music," I think and pick up my phone. Sade serenades me with "Smooth Operator" while I get undressed for a shower.

I love getting ready so much that I'm distracted from the monster in my head, though it's still doing its thing in there. I take a quick two-minute shower. Quick because I want more time to dedicate to my makeup and hair.

"I should put it up." My hair always looks good when up, and besides it's like a natural facelift. Not that I need one. I'm still only 35.

But headaches and tight elastics or clips in my hair don't mix well.

"I'll curl it," I think, musing that since I usually wear my hair straight, a new look will be well received. I bend over to grab the curling iron from under the sink and the monster in my head reminds me that he torments me as he pleases.

I let out a groan as I come up slowly to plug the curling iron in.

"Gold eyeshadow," I decide, thinking of what to do with my makeup. *"And cat-eye eyeliner."* I'm so giddy. The last time I went all out like this was at Frank's cousin's wedding, and I looked spectacular.

The rule is that if you go heavy on the eyes, you should go light on the lips.

I'm always up for breaking rules, but makeup rules I abide by. I don't want to look like a clown that's trying too hard.

"Okay I'll do lip gloss. The MAC one."

I swap Sade for a Michael Jackson playlist, and start doing my makeup. I am meticulous with the eyes. I love emphasizing my baby blues. Though I never took makeup lessons, I could put a makeup artist to shame. The end result is impeccable. My best smoky eye ever, accentuated by the gold shimmery eyeshadow. Proof that practicing something makes you really good at it. Wearing make-up every day has served me very well.

I divide my hair and start to curl it, singing my favorite song of all time along with Michael – Billie Jean.

I look so good, I could do a photoshoot for a makeup ad. I pull on my red thong and the matching bra, then look at myself in the massive mirror that's leaning against the wall. I look amazing. I slip on my stilettoes and poof, I'm transformed into a 6-foot lingerie model. Perfect hair, perfect makeup, perfect body.

Focusing on the positive makes me feel better. I don't take my looks for granted, it's taken dedication and hard work to get to the point where I am now. Moments of self-appreciation boost my motivation and remind me of the journey I've had.

"I really need to do a photoshoot," I think to myself and flex my abs, revealing a nearly perfect six pack. Nothing too obvious. Despite my "Cinderella wears Nikes" and "The gym is my home" mantras, it's imperative to me that I remain feminine above all else.

No one knew that it took skill to eat and train in a way that would keep it all in balance – to have just enough fat to be soft and feminine and just enough muscle to be athletic. My ideal look. I had cracked the code and I was proud of it.

"I should also compete," I think and turn to look at my ass. Though my arms look great and so do my legs, my ass is definitely my #1 feature and I have a long list of female haters as a result. *"Thank you God for blessing me with these amazing genes,"* I pray silently.

Next, I slip into the dress, but immediately think, *"Oh shit, how am I going to zip it up?"* The zipper goes from the top of the butt to the bottom of the neck.

"I can ask Marcus to do it," I think.

"Or Frank." I turn around and look in the mirror again. My left eyebrow rises, thoughts of enticing Frank entering my mind.

I look spectacular, but it would be awkward. So I open the French doors and sashay across the hallway to Marcus's room where the boys are playing with miniature cars.

"Baby, can you help mommy zip up the dress, please?" I ask Marcus.

They both turn towards the door when they hear my voice and their eyes widen at the sight.

"Mommyyyyyyy...," says Roman as he gets up off the floor and runs over to me, throwing his arms around my thighs. He usually reaches my hips, but since I'm 5 inches taller in my heels, my upper thighs is as high he can get.

"Mom, you look so beautiful," says Marcus, still in awe.

"Thank you, baby." I take off my shoes and walk over to kiss him, Roman still attached to me.

"Come here and give mommy a kiss," I say to Roman as I face the bed so Marcus can zip me up.

Roman jumps on the bed, facing me, and envelops me in another hug. This boy is so affectionate. I love affection and I especially love it from them.

Marcus zips up the dress, so I slip my shoes back on and start to walk out of the room. Roman runs after me and slips his hand in mine as I walk back into the master bedroom to put the finishing touches on the look – lip gloss, my oversize hoop earrings and my watch.

Then we walk downstairs hand in hand.

"Let's get this party started," I announce as we reach the main floor.

The dining room is bathed in candlelight and soft jazz music. The kitchen is where all the magic is happening. Frank is tending to the turkey when the doorbell rings.

"I'll get it," I yell out.

"Oh don't do that again," I tell myself, feeling the sharp pain in my head from the yell.

The guests arrive in groups and the street is littered with their cars.

The rest of the night is a bit blurry. People ask me questions but I miss them, unable to answer. A friend hands me a bottle of wine and a bowl of something that smells delicious, then says, "Simone, what the fuck happened to you? You look like shit."

"Oh my God, seriously? I look like shit? How?" I ask, walking over to the mirror by the front door to examine my face.

Although we both appreciate each other's honesty, this time I feel a little offended because I've put a lot of effort into how I look. I'm wearing a nice, tight dress, I've done my hair and of course my makeup is impeccable. So I know I look good. "No, I mean, you look tired and like you're not feeling well. Are you okay?" she asks, back pedaling a little.

Quickly, I collect myself. "My head is throbbing and I need a...." The word massage taunts me from the edge of my mind, refusing to be verbalized.

I go behind her, and start massaging her neck and upper back. "I just need one of these!" I say, as I let out a fake laugh to conceal my shock and embarrassment that I can't articulate the word.

"Damn it, these fucking words," I think to myself.

"It's all the wine baby. You're good," Ego reassures me.

"Mmmmm, yes, a massage would be so good. We all need one," my friend says as I massage her shoulders.

She suggests that I book an appointment to see a massage therapist tomorrow. "It'll probably help you with your headache, too."

"No way, I have another Thanksgiving shindig to go to," I tell her.

"Look at you....shindig," says Ego. *"Words are your bitches, baby. You own them. You're always the fucking boss, don't forget that,"* he adds.

"Hear, hear," I say out loud, responding to Ego.

"Hear, hear," responds my friend. "Where's my wine?"

"Let's get some," I say and link my arm with hers, pulling her towards the living room.

All night I try to exorcise the monster inside my head, with bottomless glasses of wine and a mix of Advil, Aspirin and Tylenol of various strengths, still to no avail. Plus cups of coffee over dessert. Little do I know that all I've done is energize this monster. And not a drop of water to mitigate the dehydration that sets in from the excessive wine and coffee consumption.

That's all I needed, to be dehydrated after a stroke. Dehydration thickens the blood. Definitely **not** what you want after a stroke. But I had no idea. They don't say that ignorance is bliss for no good reason.

The night is merry and everyone is having a great time. Success.

"Ha!" I rub it in to Inner Me as I head to bed.

"You can't fucking kill ME" I say triumphantly to the headache. *"But nice try."*

I enter oblivion as soon as my head hits the pillow, the room spinning. I feel like the countless glasses of wine have tamed the monster somewhat. *"Hmmmm, maybe this is why people drink on a regular basis,"* I think to myself as I float away to sleep.

"You don't lose if you get knocked down. You lose if you stay down."

Muhammad Ali

CHAPTER 4

Ignoring the Obvious ♡

Hello, wonderful Sunday! Or maybe not. The monster is back. It awakens as soon as I do. Today, it's furious and goes into high gear. It's making me pay for the liters of wine I must've consumed last night.

I didn't think it would be possible but the pain now has turned up a few notches, to an unknown scale for me. Clearly the headache was just playing yesterday. I must've provoked it with my words last night. Today, it means serious business.

I decide to do what I do best – focus on the things I need to do. And ignore the beast.

To the boys' happiness, Frank spent the night. On the couch, where he slept for months before we finally separated. He's already up, making breakfast. The smell of coffee and delicious food seduces me downstairs. "Good morning everyone," I announce as cheerfully as I can.

"Mommyyyyyy!" Roman runs to me and envelops me in a hug. I bend down and scoop him up and give him a kiss. The monster in my head does not like that one bit. Though the pain is excruciating, I carry my little boy to the table and sit down with him on my lap. My husband brings scrambled eggs, toast and the coffee pot to the table and sits down.

I'm completely unaware of what a beautiful blessing this moment is – to sit down as a family and enjoy a meal together. I very rarely had that as a child. My father was gone for work for extended periods of time. I craved meals where there would be joy and lots of laughter and togetherness.

I wish I had basked in that moment and taken it all in, let the blessing infuse me with its magic.

I realize that we have to be at my brother's house for Thanksgiving in three hours. My brother and his wife don't start to cook until the guests have arrived. And since we're family we can show up and just chat as things get done. They said to be there for 2:00 pm, which means we'd eat by 4:00 pm or 4:30 pm.

"Oh my God! It's so late!" I put Roman on the chair next to me and get up from the table far too quickly. The monster in my head punishes me for the sudden movement.

My workout alone is usually an hour and a half. Factor in travel time to the gym and back home, shower, getting ready and the travel time to get to my brother's. Three hours is definitely not enough time.

"Not that late," says Frank. "There's probably going to be some traffic, but that's okay, we'll clean up and probably only be a few minutes late."

"I need to go to the gym to burn off some of last night's calories," I tell him. "I think I'm going to ride to my brother's too."

He turns to me, shock written all over his face. His eyebrows shoot up.

"You're going to ride? You drank quite a bit last night. It's not a good idea." The concern in his voice is obvious.

"Oh, I'll be fine," I respond nonchalantly.

I grab the Advil bottle off the kitchen counter and throw four pills in my mouth. I need to sedate the headache at least a little to get through my workout, and although Advil had absolutely no effect yesterday, I try again. I wash them down with a big gulp of coffee and make my way upstairs to dress.

The gym is an absolute must today, not only because I have a hangover and because I consumed an abundance of calories last night – liberally – both liquid and solid, but I didn't get to work out at all yesterday. I also know I'm going to consume another significant amount of them today at my brother's house. Time off from the gym and thousands of calories like this – **huge** no-no in my books.

Inner Me joins forces with my husband. *"You should rest until you have to go for dinner. You also need to get the headache checked out,"* she says gently. I'm offended that she doesn't understand how crappy I feel both physically and mentally as a result of last night's onslaught of calories and therefore I **need** to work out. I ignore her.

I make my way back downstairs. Frank and the boys are still there, at the table.

"Where's Bella?" I wonder. She's nowhere in sight. I'm a bit worried about her as she has little control over her bladder. Every time she gets a little bit excited, she pees. So she needs to be walked often.

The symptoms

Marcus is eating and watching something on his iPad. "Did Bella walk for take you?" I ask him.

I stop dead in my tracks.

What I just heard myself say didn't sound correct. Even in my half-asleep, alcohol-infused stupor, I know that question is not correct. I feel that in my bones.

Something is off here.

Inner Me gasps.

"What's going on?" I ask her.

"You're not okay," she says softly.

"What do you mean I'm not okay? What's wrong with me?" Panic is quickly creeping in.

"Maybe you should go to the doctor. You still have this headache, too," she responds, completely avoiding my question.

"Huh?" asks my husband.

"What mom?" asks Marcus, concern on his face. It's the same look of concern that was there yesterday morning.

Stunned, I just stand there looking at Marcus, recounting my words. Inner Me realizes that the order of words in that sentence isn't right.

"What the hell did I just say?" I ask Inner Me.

"You said, 'Did Bella walk for take you?'" replies Inner Me.

Inner Me is absolutely brilliant, very patient with me, kind, non-judgmental and loving. And always awake. Even at 3 am when I'm going to pee. She would never turn me away and she would never be mad at me, no matter what I did, said or confessed to. She always advises me on what to do and how to proceed. Plus, she has never said "I told you so" when things turned out bad because I hadn't listened. Ego, on the other hand, is not as calm and definitely not as forgiving.

"That's not right, is it?" I ask her, concerned.

"Mom...." Marcus is still there, looking at me, waiting for an answer.

"No, no it's not," says Inner Me. *"The words aren't in the proper order."*

"Mom, are you okay?" The concern is now more evident in Marcus's voice and on his face.

"Did you take Bella for a walk? That's the right way to say it," says Inner Me.

I repeat that quickly inwardly and without hesitation I say, "Did you take Bella for a walk?" to Marcus.

"Yeah, she's in the backyard, look," says Marcus, motioning to the sliding doors. "Are you okay, though? Seriously mom." The growing worry he exhibits starts to concern me now.

"Yeah," I lie. "Wine..." I add, trailing off.

A flash of worry crosses my mind. The headache that I keep trying to tame – and it's becoming exhausting to do so – plus my new inability to string words together to formulate a proper sentence are starting to disturb me.

I promise myself to get it checked the following week. One thing at a time, though. For now, I'll get my workout done and enjoy dinner at my brother's. I'm a master of distracting myself.

Gym first. Once again, I jump on the Green Monster and make my way to Tim Hortons to get my favorite pre-workout beverage and a bagel for some quick carbs to fuel my training session. If it's not something I make myself at home, a quick coffee and a bagel with peanut butter does the trick really well. Carbs and caffeine for energy with some fat and protein. Balanced, right?

That isn't the first time my obsession with the gym overrides reason, but that's definitely the most serious one. In my mind, it's still just a really bad headache. The word stroke never even enters my mind.

I'm oblivious to the obvious. Had I known that a severe headache with no known cause was a stroke symptom, I would've been at the hospital right after the lightning strike experience in my kitchen.

Especially with the knowledge I gained from my research. The most crucial time to prevent damage from a stroke is right after it happens. The more you wait, the more you miss the window of healing or the opportunity to recover fully. All the well-known symptoms are obvious, but I ignore them.

Stroke symptoms include:

- Sudden numbness or weakness in the face, arm or leg (especially on one side of the body).

- Sudden confusion or trouble speaking or understanding speech.

- Sudden vision problems in one or both eyes.

- Sudden difficulty walking or dizziness, loss of balance or problems with coordination.

- Severe headache with no known cause.

The left side of my body seems especially weak. My left arm is tingling. And there's a constant feeling of shakiness inside. *"I've had too much coffee,"* I think, which makes perfect sense to me because I regularly consume coffee like it's water.

Since yesterday's lightning moment, I frequently stumble over my words. I can't always articulate them and it's frustrating. I don't know when this inability will strike. It comes at random. I blame the headache – it's paralyzing my thinking! And I know full well that I'm trying to cover it up to make it look like I'm okay. What I don't know is that the stroke has already damaged part of my brain. But I continue to convince myself that I'm just disoriented. *"I'll be fine. Once this headache is gone, I'll be fine,"* I keep telling myself, as I park my motorcycle. But when will the headache be gone?

"Can with small have and black I bagel coffee a peanut wheat butter?"

The cashier looks at me confused. "Excuse me?"

"Help!" I appeal to Inner Me with a sense of urgency when it hits me that nothing I said makes any sense. The words stumbled out of my mouth before I could catch them. I've placed that order so many times that it's like second nature to say the words. It's just that my brain is unable to put them in the proper order. It can get the words from the memory bank, but now, out of the blue, I just can't string them together properly.

I realize that this person didn't understand a word I just said. Okay, maybe she understood a word or maybe all the words, but she definitely did not understand the question.

Inner Me with her perfect memory repeats the sentence I just uttered again. "Can with small have and black I bagel coffee a peanut wheat butter?"

Seconds pass. They feel like hours.

"Please," I plead with Inner Me to give me the correct way to say the sentence. Poker faced, I'm just staring at the cashier, who is looking at me, waiting.

"Ma'am," she says, "Can you repeat your order please?"

"Can I have a small black coffee and a toasted whole wheat bagel with peanut butter?" says Inner Me. *"Say it like that,"* she instructs me.

"Can I have..."

"Can I have...ummm."

"A small black coffee."

"A small black coffee..."

"And a toasted..."

"And a toasted...."

"Whole wheat bagel..."

"Whole wheat bagel..."

"With peanut butter."

"With peanut butter."

Intuitively I feel the correctness of this sentence to my inner core.

"Would you like one peanut butter or two?" the cashier asks.

"Two," I say instantly, elated for a split second at the fact that I could answer this all by myself. Single word answers I can manage. Who can mess up?

"That will be three eighty," says the cashier.

"Debit," I say, elated again that I can have the conversation now all by myself, without having to run things by Inner Me.

"Go ahead," says the cashier.

I tap my bank card on the payment machine in front of me.

"You can get your order from the side, ma'am," says the young girl, motioning to her right, where filled orders are placed for people to pick up.

"Thank you," I say sweetly. One more thing I can do all by myself.

I grab my coffee and bagel and walk outside to where my motorcycle was parked. *"Oh shit,"* I think, as I see that I'd left the key in the ignition.

Not that anyone could've actually ridden off on it – how many people can operate a super-sport manual transmission motorcycle? Not many. But still, all it takes is one person that knows how to ride and they could take off with it. I push the thought out of my mind as I finish off my coffee and bagel.

"I'm fine, right?" I ask Inner Me, trying to conceal my worry. *"I mean, look, I know what this knife is for and I can use it without instruction,"* I add, referring to the plastic knife I got with my order. *"So, I'm okay, right?"*

Inner Me waits patiently for me to finish all my questions, seeing right through my *"I'm not worried or anything"* bullshit.

Before she can even answer, I say, *"I'm totally fine, it's probably just this damn headache. As soon as it's gone, I'll be right back to 100%."*

I also remind her that this is a strong headache, and even with the previous, milder ones, I wasn't able to perform 100% at work, at the gym, or anywhere for that matter.

Women can't even have sex with their husbands when they have headaches.... "Sorry honey, I have a headache," so no need to be so hard on myself for not being able to put a sentence together, right?

*"Maybe **this** coffee will help tame the monster,"* I think, knowing fully that I'm actually kidding myself. Tim Hortons does not sell magic coffee.

This is definitely the worst possible headache that anyone could have. The pain is almost excruciating. It definitely is excruciating, even for my really high pain threshold. *"You gave birth twice,"* Ego jumps in, to remind me of my strength and ability to overcome, *"to two boys, neither of whom was small. This is just a headache. Suck it up, you'll be fine."*

"That's right," I say triumphantly to Inner Me, and I shut down the conversation by placing the earbuds in my ears and pressing play to start the music on my phone.

I throw the almost empty coffee cup in the trash can, put my helmet on and jump back on my bike. *"This helmet is so tight, it's not helping with this headache,"* I think. *"Ummmmm suck it up, buttercup,"* Ego says to me again. *"You're totally fine. Remember, you are not a victim and you gave birth twice. Pain is your bitch, okay?"*

A mistake

I pull up at the gym and park in my usual spot – up on the sidewalk. I remove my helmet, full of confidence, because the sexiness of a woman dancing with a machine makes up for missing earrings, messy hair or no makeup. Silently I'm praying that I won't experience a repeat performance of yesterday's "workout". I'm more jittery than I've ever been. *"Whoa, that is some strong caffeine,"* I think as I walk to the women's change room.

I have tried all the legal supplements in the fitness world – pre-workout powders, post-workout or recovery powders, during the workout powders, hydrating drinks like Gatorade, fat burners and creatine. Coffee is still my favorite pre-workout beverage and I've started hydrating with water mixed with a little bit of fruit juice or honey. Natural is always better.

I want to keep to my routine so badly because this is something familiar, something I feel so good doing, and the gym is a place where I always get the empowerment I need. So in a way, coming to the gym is very logical – I want to feel better, so I do all the things that have made me feel better before. I'm doing my thing. Pushing through. Nothing new.

Working out helped me tremendously with labor and birth both times. It's thanks to those kinds of workouts that my body was strong and ready for those significant events. And I have such fond memories. To this day I still laugh at the horrified looks on women's faces when they saw me doing squats with my full-term belly, warning me that I'd give birth on the gym floor. Marcus decided that he wasn't making his debut in the world until he was good and ready, so he went over the due date. And I went to the gym up until I had him. Heck, I even resorted to old wives' tales like drive on a very bumpy road to start labor. Marcus had none of it. Neither the gym, nor the bumpy road deterred him from coming into the world when he was ready – 5 days after the due date.

You can't be ready for a stroke, though. Stroke is all neurological and chemical. The body goes through incredible shock during stroke and that kind of shock is not built into the body the way labor and birth are. The body innately knows that birth is a possibility – it's the only way procreation can take place, after all, so it's built for it; stroke, on the other hand is not built in.

The brain chemistry alters to accommodate the damage, and the healthy parts of the brain compensate to ensure that the body is functioning at as close to 100% as possible given the circumstances. In its infinite wisdom, the body does what is necessary to survive and function. Especially after something as huge as stroke. As I still had no idea that what had transpired the previous morning was a stroke, I was expecting to do the things I'd been capable of so far.

I've stopped beating myself up because of the things I didn't know. Could've and would've don't change a thing. My past is not going to change because I feel regret.

Back on the gym floor, I walk back over to the leg press machine, ready to show it who's boss, which is what I've always done. I have been so patient building strength and power in my legs. I know that big, compound movements are the path to muscular, strong and powerful shapely legs.

My failed attempt at doing legs yesterday doesn't deter me. I convince myself that yesterday was just an off day.

Not true. Today is worse. The pain is stronger than my will, though I never thought that was even possible. After a couple of unsuccessful attempts at loading the machine with my usual warm-up weight, I move over to a bench and attempt to do some sit-down squats while holding weights in my hands – an exercise I'd used numerous times with my new personal training clients. This is a far cry from what I usually do.

My legs are shaking and the tiny dumbbells feel like they weigh 1000 pounds each.

I set them back on the rack, grab my bag and head to the change room, fighting back tears.

I hate that I can't do a proper workout. At no point do I even stop to question why all of a sudden I can no longer do what my body has done for years with ease. It can't even do a fraction of it. I can't do **anything** in here. I pour all my energy into the disappointment instead of questioning what's going on so I can address it.

Defeated, I leave the gym. As I'm riding home, I start to acknowledge that maybe this is not an ordinary headache after all. *"On Tuesday, when the holidays are over,"* I promise myself.

The last warnings

I get back home. Nobody's there. I hate the emptiness of the house. It's so perfectly furnished and arranged. The mirrors, the leather couches, the beautiful dining set, the regal four-poster king size bed majestically commanding presence in the master bedroom. The French doors, the 2-inch thick granite countertops, the massive bathtub. But none of it matters. I want my family in it. I don't recognize what that feeling of longing is so I push it away and I rush to the walk-in closet, where I change quickly.

"Bellaaaaa," I call out, wondering if she was left home for me to bring with me to my brother's. I listen for the bark or her nails tapping on the hardwood floor. Nothing. Frank and the kids must've taken her with them.

Sometimes I have conversations with Bella when we're alone. I tell her all my sorrows and all my secrets. She also sees me picking my nose and with skincare masks on my face. She's my most trusted confidante aside from Inner Me and Ego.

She sometimes makes being alone in this huge house more bearable.

I shift my attention to pondering again whether I should take my car or the motorcycle. Since it's the weekend and the boys would be staying with Frank, I decide on the motorcycle, even though I'm not particularly fond of riding at night and I feel I should take something to my brother's, at least a bottle of wine. *"I'll take a backpack,"* I think to myself.

The beast in my head is likely on a break now. Either that or I've gotten so accustomed to the pain it inflicts upon me that I don't know how to operate without it any longer. The monster has become part of me. It's with me every second of every minute of every hour.

In my jeans and leather jacket, wine in my backpack, I head out, listening to my favorite Dr. Dre song, my motorcycle-riding anthem.

I zoom right past Frank's car on the highway as I do all the crazy stuff I've learned since I started riding, like splitting lanes and using exit lanes to pass other cars. I don't do these things because I want to show off, I do them because I'm confident in my riding abilities and know I can. I also think it's useless to ride a motorcycle that can do so much and not experience at least some of the things it can do or some of the things you can do with it.

I reach my brother's well before Frank. He drives an SUV and since he has the boys in the car, I know he won't speed.

My youngest niece greets me at the door. She's like a little angel – feminine and so sweet. I love her and her little angelic, girly voice. As soon as I walk in, I scoop her up to give her a hug. My head does not like that one bit. I put her down quickly, feeling like I'm going to faint, my blood pressure dropping hard.

"Don't do that again!" Ego warns me.

I listen to my niece tell me all about something she drew and who she made it for, trying to act normal, so that nobody could see that I feel far, far from normal. I don't ever want anyone to know I'm vulnerable or weak. Especially my family. My mother would worry and I don't want to put that kind of stress on her.

"You should've stayed home to rest. You really are not well at all. And you really need to get this checked out. It's still happening. This headache is not going away, Simone," says Inner Me gently.

"Yeah, we already agreed. I'm gonna do this, right after the weekend," I respond. *"I promise."*

And I really mean that. I have full intention of looking into it. Despite my toughness and push-through-it attitude, I'm wondering why this headache isn't going away and what it's all about. I've never had a headache that lasted more than a few hours.

Somehow, I survive dinner at my brother's and I have them all fooled, since no one says anything. I don't stay late and since I came on the motorcycle, I drink water the whole time. Had I driven the car I would've likely indulged in a glass of alcohol, but my #1 rule with the motorcycle is NO ALCOHOL WHEN I RIDE. EVER!

The headache offers no reprieve on my way home. The only time I don't feel the pain is when I sleep, so I look forward to getting to bed.

"Maybe you can call Telehealth or do some research about really bad headaches," suggests Inner Me as I lie down.

"No way. I'm too tired. I want to sleep," I tell her.

"You can do it when you wake up."

"I'm going to Frank's tomorrow. Last Thanksgiving dinner. And then I'm going straight to the doctor. I promise."

Sleep comes as soon as I close my eyes.

"Everything in excess is opposed to nature."

Hippocrates

CHAPTER 5

Fighting for my Life

It's Monday. I allow myself to sleep in. It's a holiday so the gym is closed. Even if I wanted to go I can't.

I wake up slowly and decide to take a bath and read a little. A little bit of pampering. I turn on the water and pour in some lavender scented Epsom salt, then step in, book in hand. I love to read. This is a habit I formed when I was little. I became a voracious reader and I would read anything I could get my hands on. It was always stories of fairies and princesses, dragons, castles and magical lands. I loved losing myself in the worlds of those stories. They sure beat the reality of the brutal communist regime that was harsh, cruel and devoid of compassion. There was nothing that I loved doing as much as reading. The sound of my mom's voice giving me shit because I would stay up too late to read still echoes in my mind now, when I tell myself *"one more chapter"*, just as I did as a child. Playing with my friends came a close second, but reading was my religion.

Though it's hard to concentrate with the monster in my head punishing me every moment, I manage to lose myself in Jules Verne's world for an hour. I could read on, but since the hot water has run out, I need to get out and get going.

The thing about me is that I can get ready in 15 minutes if I want to – hair, makeup and getting dressed – or go all out and take two hours.

The silence in the house is deafening. I hate it. So I turn on the music on my phone as I get dressed.

"I'm going to make it a 15-minute thing," I tell myself.

"Please take the car today," says Inner Me softly.

"I will," I answer instantly. *"I'm bringing the boys back with me."*

"Thank you, God," she adds.

Not only is she kind and compassionate and patient, she is also funny when she wants to be.

Despite the soothing bath and sleeping in, I'm exhausted. Not tired – exhausted. I have no strength, no power and no energy. I am struggling. I'm glad it's Monday and that Thanksgiving is almost over.

Though I love celebrations, I hate being off my routine and my diet. I've eaten way too much already, drunk more than I should drink in an entire year and I haven't had a workout in three days.

I don't ever take time off from the gym unless it's closed. The last time I missed the gym was when I gave birth to Roman, and that was obviously not voluntary.

I'm anxious to get to Frank's house and be among his family. It takes me back to when we were together and doing the family thing. I get to see the boys, too. I miss them already. This is how Frank must feel when he's away from them and this is clearly how the boys feel when they're away from him.

The day is fun and I indulge in a glass of wine with dinner. The food is plentiful and rich.

"I can't wait to get back to my healthy eating," I think to myself.

Getting back to the house with the boys that evening makes me happy. They're there with me and getting things ready for the short week ahead keeps me busy, preoccupied and distracted from the emotional pain in my heart and the crazy pain in my head.

The massive king size bed in the master bedroom accommodates all three of us and I'm glad the boys want to sleep there, because they're near me and I can protect them should something happen.

The morning comes quickly. Being grateful for small things feels so good. I forget my troubles when I'm in a state of gratitude. If only I would've practiced that more often. Today I can finally go to the gym and eat clean. But first things first – breakfast for the boys and their school lunches. The school is a three-minute walk from the house, literally around the corner, so luckily no commute to take into account for them. My commute all the way downtown was another story, but I'm going to work out of one of the satellite offices today. The perks of working for the government.

Besides, I'm too exhausted to drive all the way downtown in bumper-to-bumper traffic, which was a daily thing for me. And imagine doing that with the headache I have. I shudder at the thought as I make my way down to the kitchen.

The level of mental and physical exhaustion I feel at this point is indescribable. I blame the busy weekend, and the headache. Pain is extremely taxing on the body. It's exactly why people become addicted to painkillers.

"Maybe I should call in sick today," I think to myself. *"At least I could clean the house properly."*

I love this house but it has been such a chore since we bought it – a huge lot with lots of lush, green grass that needs to be cut, four large bedrooms and four washrooms that need to be cleaned regularly, a large dining room that loves dust and a kitchen that feels like it's open 24 hours a day to make whatever the kids want – like popcorn at 9:30 pm. And since my own party on Saturday, I haven't had a chance to clean properly and put things away.

The idea of how much work it will be to clean this house all by myself overwhelms me, especially after I feel like I've done a full day's work just getting breakfast and lunches made for the boys. My exhaustion is off the charts at this point. And it's still very early in the morning.

I kiss the boys and wish them a great day at school, then decide to sit on the couch for five minutes to catch my breath and strategize for the day.

"The monster must've grown and taken over my whole body," I think to myself. I haven't consumed anything yet and I feel so shaky that even just standing up is now hard to do. *"Maybe my blood sugar is low,"* I think, which is ridiculous because I ate quite late last night at Frank's and all the nutrients are still circulating in my blood.

"Please, I beg you, call work and tell them you're sick," pleads Inner Me. *"You can't go in, you're not well and you promised you'd have the headache looked at today,"* she adds.

She's right. And getting this headache looked at by a doctor is a good enough reason to call in sick.

I stand up to get my phone. My knees feel like overcooked spaghetti as I walk the short distance to the kitchen. As soon as I get there, I plop into a chair. One more step and I would've fallen.

The idea that something is terribly wrong with me finally sinks in and sheer panic takes over. I haven't even considered how exactly I would get to the doctor's office; how would I drive myself there feeling like this? How would

I walk to the car in the garage and how would I walk to the doctor's office from the parking lot? As I'm trying to decide whether to call the office first or the doctor, the ding of a text message interrupts my thoughts. Thankfully, I don't have to stand up again to get my phone.

"It's probably Frank checking to see if the boys are off to school all okay," I think. It is.

The doorbell rings.

"Who's here so early in the morning?" I wonder.

I don't even get a chance to get up off the chair when I hear the door open. I hadn't locked it after the boys left.

"Goooooood morning!" I hear my friend yell out.

I recognize her voice.

"Hey Gina," I answer, trying to sound as cheerful as she does, failing miserably.

She makes her way to the kitchen, purse and keys in hand.

The look of shock on her face is evident as soon as she lays eyes on me.

"What's the matter?" she asks, grave concern in her voice.

"Nothing, why?" I lie in as normal a tone as I can muster.

"You don't look good at all," she says, her eyes scanning me as if to see something physical that would identify what's wrong with me.

"Oh, I know, I got no sleep last night and since Saturday, all I've done is eat lots of crap and drink," I say. Though it's a lie, all of that makes sense and I feel my earlier panic lift slightly. *"I feel like shit because of all the shit I ate and all the alcohol is still in my system,"* I think to myself.

The worry on her face is replaced by relief. That alone puts me more at ease.

"What's up?" I ask her, still wondering why she's here.

"Well, I thought we'd get a head start. We'll be done by eleven," she says.

"Did you make coffee?" She asks, walking towards the fridge, "I know you're always dieting and all, but do you happen to have cream? You know I loooooove cream in my coffee." She turns towards me, her blond curls bouncing.

"Where's your coffee?" She doesn't even give me a chance to respond to her first question. Gina's energy seems impossible to keep up with.

"I was thinking, we can do each room together or I can take one room and you take another. But I want to chat, so let's do each room together," she suggests, leaning over on the countertop.

I have absolutely no idea what she's talking about.

"Well?" she asks, her perfect eyebrows shooting up.

I give her a blank stare. The monster inside my head shoots a dagger in my temple. I stifle a groan. I can't let Gina think I'm not okay.

"Oh my God, did you forget?" she asks. "We made plans at the party that I'd come help you clean today, remember? Or do you have alcohol-induced amnesia?" she continues, and lets out a laugh. I look at her and give a weak laugh too. Who can laugh through this kind of pain?

"I guess I do. I don't remember that at all," I say. Truthfully, I have no recollection of us making plans for her to come help me clean, but I know she wouldn't lie about something like this.

"Okay, well, we made the plans, so let's get started."

"Where's the coffee?" she asks again. "Looks like I'll have to use your 2% milk," she adds, rolling her eyes.

"It's in the other cupboard to the left of the fridge," I answer, trying hard to keep my focus on our conversation and away from the monster thrashing about inside my skull.

"Let's start with the dining room. I see that all the wine glasses are on the table," she says. "Let's put them in the credenza first. Just to make sure they're safe. I'm surprised you haven't knocked any over."

"How? I've barely been here. I've been from one party to the next," I say, continuing to pretend I'm okay while the monster turns the pain up a few notches.

"Shit. I think I left my phone in my car," says Gina as she rifles through her purse. "I told my mother-in-law to call me. I have to drive her to get something she put on hold, all the way in Richmond Hill," she adds, rolling her eyes.

Gina loves to roll her eyes.

"That's why I wanted to get done early, babe. I'll be back," she says as she grabs her keys and walks out of the kitchen.

She's right about those wine glasses. They won't be safe on the table once the boys come back from school. Sometimes they pretend they're Jedis or Sith and a battle ensues. Fragile glasses could easily be destroyed by Darth Vader in the middle of a Stars Wars battle. Or by a fight over who would be Darth Vader this time.

I decide to get a head start on them, completely forgetting that I haven't called the office to tell them I'm not coming in. All I'm trying to do now is distract myself from the pain in my head and not let Gina down, since I planned to have her over to help me clean my house.

As I start walking towards the dining room my knees remind me that they're overcooked spaghetti.

I never make it.

"Health is the greatest of human blessings."

Hippocrates

CHAPTER 6
Coming Back ♡

My eyelid is pulled up and a light is flashed into my eye. "Stroke! Get her to CT stat."

"WHAT???? STROKE???? Did he just say STROKE???" The word stroke hits me like a 1000-foot tsunami on a sandy, sunny beach.

I knew very well what a stroke was - damage to the brain from interruption of its blood supply. A cerebrovascular accident. A massive medical emergency.

Nobody in my family has had a stroke before. Nobody. There's been cancer and diabetes, but not one single family member has ever had a stroke. I am the first one. The only person I personally know who's had a stroke is my mother-in-law. But I'm not genetically related to her. I'm just married to her baby boy, so she didn't genetically pass the risk on to me. And our lifestyles couldn't have been more different. I live a very healthy lifestyle. That's something I'm absolutely sure of. But if I just had a stroke too, could I die like she did?

Even though I'm completely disoriented and in utter shock, I notice that I'm in the hospital, surrounded by medical people. I have an IV in my arm and I'm hooked up to numerous beeping machines. I'm on a stretcher, wearing a flimsy hospital gown. They've undressed me. That takes time, and they need to move fast in a life and death situation. They don't have time to take your clothes off. So they had actually cut off my clothes, including one of my favorite shirts. My favorite beautiful blue Lululemon shirt. I loved it so much.

After the CT scan, I notice Frank. He's here. I feel slight comfort. Having someone in your corner is such a powerful and important thing. I want to run to him and cry, tell him I'm so scared and ask him what's happening. I want to feel his arms around me, telling me everything is okay and that I'll be fine.

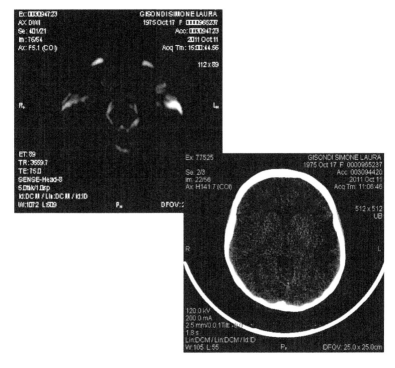

SIMONE L. GISONDI, CHNC

The look on his face is forever etched on my mind – a mix of grave concern, incredible worry and fear. Anna. His mother. She had a stroke. And she died as a result.

I'm alive. But she didn't die right after her stroke. She was found in her home, having had a stroke while she was alone. The thought sends a cold chill up my spine. She died later. Just like I could.

Frank is reliving the nightmare. First his mother, now the mother of his children.

How could I possibly have had a stroke, of all things? I'm half Anna's age! And I'm in a hospital.

She died in a hospital. I was never afraid of hospitals before but now I don't feel safe in one at all.

Like an underwater current, panicky thoughts pull me into a tight hug of terror. I never knew what it meant to have a million thoughts in a millisecond. Now I do. They're all racing, competing for my attention. I can't put them into words. I cannot verbalize them to even ask a question. The thoughts of death take over and grip me so tightly I can barely breathe. One of the machines is measuring my heart rate. 177. It is racing. This situation is life threatening, for sure. But I'm not resting. I'm worried. Actually, I'm scared. I'm scared for my life.

I'm convinced I'm not in a safe place. The only person I know who had a stroke didn't survive. The first stroke happened at home, but the subsequent ones happened in the hospital and she still couldn't be saved. So I could very easily die, too. I could have another stroke. Or many. Do I want to die? Do I want to die in a hospital?

I might have already had another stroke. What if I have a few more? What are they going to do? Am I really going to die like Anna? Where are the boys? I want to see them **now**. Where's my mom? Did anyone call her to tell her I just had a stroke? What about dad? Did someone tell him?

Holy shit, stroke!!!!! Stroke is **REALLY** serious. Oh my God, I could die. Oh, fuck, this just got serious. Why didn't I just go to the hospital when the headache started? Inner Me begged and pleaded. Why didn't I listen?

I don't even think of the headache anymore. That's long gone, part of what feels like a very distant past. Now, I'm in the bubble of a stroke. I forget my headache, I forget about the party, failed workouts in the gym and how I rode the Green Monster. All I have is the thought that I had a stroke and that I could die. I'm now the most scared for my life I have ever been.

"Okay, just take a deep breath and relax," I tell myself. *"Let's break this down. What does this all mean?"*

Okay, so I had a stroke. When did this stroke happen? Was it when I got hit by lightning inside my head or when I went to put the glasses back in the credenza?

Wait! What exactly happened there? That's the last thing I remember, heading into the dining room to get started on the glasses while Gina went to get her phone. What happened after? I search my mind for a memory of something that happened after.

Nothing comes up.

"Where's Gina?" I wonder. I'm sure she can tell me what happened.

"I could have another stroke and die." There goes another death thought, bullying its way to the forefront of my mind.

"That's not a fact," I say defiantly to the thought.

"Where the hell are Inner Me and Ego?" I wonder. *"Have they abandoned me at such a crucial time? Leaving me to face this mess and these horrible thoughts all by myself?"*

"I'm okay, I'm in the hospital." I say to that same horrible thought.

*"Right, like Anna was. In the hospital. Where she **died**,"* retorts the evil thought.

"Not the same hospital," I say, defiant again.

*"No, but she was in a **very** good hospital. Didn't they use a helicopter to take her there, because it was a better hospital than the one she was initially taken to? Remember? She was on life support,"* the thought taunts me.

"But we saw her alive," I say.

"Yes, artificially alive, and she still died right after," the thought responds, continuing to taunt me.

I had no idea that I was empowering this damn thing and making it grow by giving attention to it and engaging it in conversation in my head.

"Do you know why they have a morgue here?" it continues, without even giving me a chance to respond. *"Because people die in hospitals **all the time**,"* it says.

I burst into tears. The fact is that I **could** die. In fact, I **may** die. Stroke is a known killer after all. Cardiovascular disease is the leading cause of death, especially here in North America.

With every sentence, with every repetition, I dig a bigger hole for myself. Every negative aspect I know about stroke and hospitals is like another slap, another kick, another punch to bring me down. I am emotionally battered.

I thought I was scared when I was home, worried that someone would break in. Ha!!! I had no idea what being scared was. I do now.

I'm scared for my life.

I don't fall back on my usual self-talk, where I might say, *"Oh, I had a stroke. But that's okay. I'm in good hands. Okay, so what do we do now?"*

"Fuck that, that's not how I feel," I think. *"I want some fucking answers, **now**."*

"Excuse me," I say to one of the nurses. "Is Gina here?"

She completely ignores me, as she's adding a second bag of something to the IV pole.

"Excuse me," I say louder.

She turns to me.

"Is Gina here?" I ask again.

"You're in the resuscitation room. No one is allowed in here to see you. Rest," she says and walks away.

The others are busy with the machines, writing on charts and talking to each other.

It's freezing. I need a blanket.

"Excuse me," I appeal to another nurse, who looks kinder and more motherly.

"Yes dear?" she says, turning to me.

"I'm cold," I say to her.

She takes a blanket from a cabinet and starts covering me with it.

"I want to see my husband."

It feels so good to call him my husband. It means that I'm not alone. I don't want to be alone.

"Where's your husband?" she asks me.

"He's outside," I reply, my voice full of gratitude.

"What's his name?"

"Frank," I tell her.

She walks out of the resuscitation room and returns within seconds, Frank following behind.

"Hi Simone." Worry is etched on his face.

I remember the look in his eyes. I'm momentarily transported back to November 7, 2003, at the hospital where his mother was, completely unresponsive, on life support. The worry. The fear. The sadness. All mixed together.

"Are you okay?" he asks.

"I'm scared." Tears bathe my eyes.

He grabs my hand and gives it a squeeze.

"You're in good hands," he says, not so convincing.

"Is Gina here?"

"No. No sense in her being here."

"How did you find out that I'm here?"

I need to know what happened at the house. How did I get here? How did Frank find out?

"I'm your emergency contact, remember?" he says, looking around at all the machines in the room.

"So they called you," I say.

"Yes."

"How did I get here?"

"By ambulance," he says, turning to look at me again.

"Where are the boys? Do they know I'm here?" More tears fill my eyes.

What a mess. I was so looking forward to getting back to routine. Being in the hospital was not part of my plan.

"They're at school. No, they don't know. Don't worry, I'll get them from school. You just concentrate on getting better," he says, trying to sound reassuring.

I know the boys will be okay with him, but I don't want them to know I'm here, that I had a stroke.

"Please don't tell them about this," I blurt out. Deep inside I know there's no way I can hide the fact that I had a stroke from my kids, nor do I want to lie to them, but isn't it enough that the family life they had growing up was gone? Now they have to deal with the fact that their mother is in the hospital because she had a stroke? They're too young to deal with such big things.

I so desperately want to protect them from having their hearts broken more with this news.

"Simone, of course I'm going to tell them. How are we going to explain to them that you're hospitalized?" he answers calmly. He's right.

"Oh my God! Work!!!" I exclaim, remembering that I was supposed to call to let them know I had a doctor's appointment. Not so far off. I'm definitely with a doctor. Or a few.

"They know, don't worry," he says.

"Sir, I'm going to ask you to wait outside," says a man in a white coat.

Frank lets go of my hand and walks out of the room.

"No, I want him to stay here," I protest to the doctor.

I want Frank to hear all they say and see what they do to me. If something should happen, I want him to know. Or if they say something that I won't remember, he will.

I'm too deep in fear for my memory to function. Though he seems calm, Frank is scared too.

I'm sure going through this again is no easy feat for him.

"We have to run some tests," says the doctor, looking at the numbers the machines are reporting. "We can't have visitors in here," he adds.

"Visitors? This guy's on some serious Kool-Aid. Who the fuck visits someone in the resuscitation room? Get me the hell out of here," I think, completely annoyed and downright pissed at this doctor.

"No, I want him here," I insist sternly. "Frank," I call out.

Having worked in healthcare was a Godsend right about now. I know that they can't deny my request. I'm scared and I need my emotional support.

"This guy is acting like he's operating on me," I think, my annoyance increasing.

"He can come right back in as soon as we're done. There's not enough room in here," says the doctor, not even looking at me.

That's the thing with some doctors, they're completely disrespectful, devoid of emotion and compassion, with massive God complexes and tripping on their self-imposed power.

Not a single kind word, not a single care about how scared I am and that having a family member in the room gives me comfort.

"Who needs a family member when I have you, right?" I retort, sarcastically.

He ignores me and turns to one of the nurses to bark an order, then leaves the room. Four nurses are left to tend to me.

"Please, can my husband come back?" I ask the same nurse who brought Frank in last time.

"We just have to run some tests, and I promise I'll have him right back in," she responds, kindness in her voice.

"What tests?" I ask.

"Some blood tests and then we have to take you down the hall for a few more tests we can't do in here. I promise you'll see your husband," she adds, smiling warmly.

"Okay," I say, giving her a weak smile. I like her. And I trust her.

As they go through their procedures, I lie there, my eyes fixed on the ceiling, trying to stem the new wave of negative thoughts rushing to the forefront of my mind, colliding into each other, vying for my attention.

"We must know that both pleasure and joy, as well as sadness and anger come from our thoughts."

Hippocrates

CHAPTER 7

Building my Alcatraz ♡

They keep telling me that they can't put me in a room yet because they don't have one available. That's why I'm on this stretcher. In a hallway. Alone.

What day is it? It's been a few nights for sure. I have no idea. I can't sleep. I want to sleep. It's not comfortable to sleep on a stretcher. Okay, it's better than the floor, but how am I supposed to heal and get better if I can't get restful sleep? I have so many questions, none of which ever get answered.

More than anything I wish for silence. Complete silence. I'd like to sit with my mind and make sense of all this somehow. I really need time to dissect and process all this.

I can't do that here in the hospital with the noise from machines, the constant code red, pink and blue announcements and the odd code white. I don't fully understand who is who, what they do and why they do what they do to me. It's a constant stream of doctors, nurses, therapists, porters and technicians. The days blur into each other, endlessly.

The lights in the hospital hallway are really bright. How is anybody supposed to sleep here? Or better yet, to get better...to heal?

I don't know it now, but in about three years, when I go back to school and study about health, I find out that my initial thoughts are right: you're supposed to sleep in a very dark room to release melatonin – a hormone – which is **crucial** for brain detoxification. The brain can't detoxify itself quickly enough, and over time, neurodegenerative disease begins if that detoxification doesn't take place, which melatonin is needed for. The body can only produce melatonin in complete darkness, which you never get in a hospital. So when I say that you can't heal in a hospital, trust me, **you literally can't**. People die in hospitals, they don't heal. Sure, they get better – at best - but they don't heal. You can't heal when you can't sleep!

The thoughts in my head about the stroke, my situation and my possible future are all intertwined and blurred, much like the days I spend in the hospital. Everything is repetitive. I'm in a never-ending loop that's scary and out of my control. I don't know what day of the week it is and how much more time I have to serve, as I call it – because that's what it feels like, serving prison time.

Maybe I'm a clinical study subject, being somewhat of a unique stroke victim, having had a stroke at such a young age. What if stroke killed **after** the fact? If that's the case, I could die right now, tonight in my sleep, tomorrow, the day after, next week.... Is there a timeline for the second stroke?

"Get rest, Simone. It will take time for you to get better," I'm told over and over when I ask that question. Like it's even possible to actually get rest in the prison this hospital has become. In fact, being in the hospital is actually worse, because in prison at least inmates get to go outside. I haven't breathed in nature's fresh air in God knows how long. Being on a stretcher in the hallway, and nowhere near a window I haven't seen the outside world in what feels like years.

It's no wonder I understand so little of what they say to me, when they actually even take the time to answer me. They look at me as someone whose brain is damaged, so they discount me as someone who cannot understand, someone mentally handicapped.

The communication issues are backed by the lack of collaboration in my brain, plus the medical jargon. I never lost the ability to speak but I'm having a lot of trouble articulating. Mechanically, I can do it. I can move my lips, tongue and vocal chords, but my words still jumble from time to time. That happens without warning and without rhyme or reason.

All this aside, my mind is operating at 100%, 100% of the time.

Conversations

"Tell me what this is, Simone." The doctor is holding out her left fist, pointing to her knuckle with the index finger of her right hand. She is so lovely, so kind and patient. I look over to Jowita for help. My amazing friend, who left work to be at my side.

I like this doctor. She smiles at me softly and nods her head encouragingly.

Seconds that feel like aeons elapse.

She's still tapping her knuckle. Jowita is sitting patiently. The medical student that accompanies the doctor like a shadow is writing notes on a clipboard. I have no idea what the student is writing, but it's the doctor's judgement that I fear most. Will she give me a death sentence? Will she tell me that this is really nothing to worry about?

Deep in my mind I know the word. I know how to describe it, I know what it's made of, I even know how to spell it. K-N-U-C-K-L-E. Knuckle.

I stare blankly at the doctor trying to push the word out of my mind through my mouth. Silence.

This is the most vulnerable I've felt since being admitted to the ER and wearing nothing but a hospital gown. I stare blankly at her as she fires off her next question.

"Okay, let's try this instead," she says and takes a pen from the breast pocket of her lab coat. She holds the pen in front of me. "What's this, Simone?" I see what she is doing. She likely thinks that a simpler, one syllable word is easier for me to articulate than the harder, two syllable word that's comprised of an aphthong.

I sit on the hospital bed looking at the pen, knowing what it is and what it's used for, but powerless to utter the word. More seconds that feel like aeons pass.

"IT'S A DAMN PEN!!!! IT'S A FUCKING PEN!!!! PEEEN!!!!!!" I think in sheer exasperation.

My brain has zero interest in participating in this. My entire verbal communication system is waiting for the brain to get things in motion. I consciously know that my brain is functioning on some level because I'm able to understand the fact that I'm in the hospital, that I'm not leaving to go home anytime soon and that I suffered a stroke. I also understand that a question is being asked of me, and that an answer is expected. I know the answer. I knew it a nanosecond after it was asked.

I'm able to process this whole event with 100% ability. On a superficial level I know very well what's going on here. However, this whole thing and all its intricacies are happening faster than my mind can fully grasp and translate so that I have a full understanding of what's actually taking place. That's only because I know absolutely nothing about stroke in 35-year-olds.

The words I need are literally on the edge of my mind and my memory is able to make the connection between the physical items in front of my eyes and the words assigned to them. In fact, I also know them in Romanian. This is a repeat performance of that moment at the party when the word massage taunted me from the edge of my mind, stubbornly refusing to be spoken.

I give up. I let out a breath of defeat and hang my head low. Out of the corner of my eye, I glimpse a stack of paper towels on the nightstand by the bed.

"COME ON SIMONE, YOU KNOW THE DAMN WORD!" Ego yells at me. *"Write it down on that paper towel at least. Unless you want to look stupid. You* **know** *you're not stupid. Do you want them to laugh at you? Or worse yet, feel sorry for you?"*

Ego is speaking now and it's downright mean. I always enjoyed how he pushed me, but I don't need this right now. I reach for the doctor's pen, grab the paper towels and write, shakily, in capital letters, PEN. She looks at my pathetic effort and then looks up at me.

"You can't say it?" she asks.

I shake my head.

"Possible partial Broca and anomic aphasia," she says, turning to the student who was still writing furiously.

Her foreign words struck panic in me. *"What is that?"* I ask Inner Me. The anxiety this is causing me is not helpful. If anything, it's making things worse. Why is nothing explained to **me**? All that ever happens is endless questioning, interrogation. What would the repercussions of failing these endless tests be? Why is everything being written on a chart? Are all patients left to wonder what the hell is going on like I am? Is every other patient wondering if they're a complete idiot, like I feel after every interrogation that I fail, with no explanation? Do all other patients feel stripped of their dignity, like they're not considered worthy of reassurance and compassion, of an explanation of what's going on? Or is it just me?

So I keep asking myself the same questions with the belief that they make more sense than the fact that I'm very different from other stroke patients. That not everybody wants to hear all this. That we all have our ways of healing and dealing with illnesses.

My thoughts make sense to me, and that's all that matters at this point. After all, my mind is sharp as a razor, remember? Am I even going to see my kids again? Will my custody be taken away from me? Will I be institutionalized? Will I be able to work? Drive?

Since being imprisoned in this dark hospital, I've started to understand more of the Me's that are working with me, because they have been my constant companions and because I can talk with them easily and with no impediment. It's so much easier to interface with the inner part of me than it is to interface with the outer world.

I come back to the present moment where the doctor is talking to the student as if I'm not even in the room.

"Aphasia....what the hell is aphasia?" I ask Inner Me and Ego. *"And the other stuff she said, what is that?"*

"Hmmm, I don't know," Inner Me replies, confirming that after searching the memory bank for the words and/or the meanings, I've never come into contact with any of those terms. *"It's medical jargon,"* she adds.

"Well, I need to learn about them. I'm sure it's just another diagnosis," I tell Inner Me, with a depressed tone.

Though Frank's mom also had a stroke, she never regained consciousness and the ability to speak, so none of these diagnoses were ever mentioned when we spoke with her doctors.

Jowita is watching the doctor and the student intently. Knowing her as I do, I'm sure she wants to hear as much as she can so that she can help me. She's an amazing friend. Here she is, spending her time in the hospital with me, when she could actually spend it doing something she enjoys. I know with absolute certainty that she does **not** enjoy hospitals and they're the last place you'd catch her.

Jowita's presence comforts me so much. I wish she would stay with me. I need someone here, because if I die in my sleep, who would know? Death thoughts creep back in, reminding me that many people have died and continue to die in hospitals. This hospital, like all other hospitals, has a morgue. I'm literally sharing the building with dead people, with people that are dying and people that are sicker than I am. *"I'm 100% sure no one has ever **truly** healed here,"* I think.

"Get some rest, Simone," says the doctor with a warm, kind smile, squeezing my shoulder gently. With that, she walks out of my room, the student close behind her. I manage a half smile. I still know nothing, and this new word "aphasia" increases my anxiety.

"Can I?" I ask Jowita, reaching for her iPhone. I want to Google "aphasia", so I can understand it and store it in my memory bank.

As I find out later, anomic aphasia refers to the brain's speech center's inability to retrieve words and failure to express them, which is exactly what's happening to me. The most frustrating part of this aphasia is that it's inconsistent and unreliable.

"Why is my brain failing me like this? Why is my brain refusing to cooperate with my verbal communication system?" I ask Ego and Inner Me.

"Girlie, you really should get some rest," Jowita says, standing up to go before they could answer.

I know that it's out of concern, but why the hell is everyone telling me to rest? I need to know what I'm dealing with here. I need to overcome this challenge and I need to understand the dimensions of it. I'm competitive and active, I have **never** been passive. Why are people expecting me to be what I am not and have never been? Why is everyone expecting me to act against the very way I am? I can't rest when there's so much I want to know. Dealing with challenges is when I thrive, when I'm at my best.

"Nooooo, don't go!" I want to scream. I hate being in this damn place all alone. I am all alone, because unless your loved ones are there with you, you really are alone, despite the hundreds of people scurrying around – porters, cleaners, nurses, doctors, students, EMS personnel and the odd executive.

But I understand that people still have jobs and bills to pay, so I don't ask anyone to put their life on hold to come and babysit me.

"I'll be back tomorrow," she says.

And then, with the warmest smile, she adds, "And you know what we'll do? I'll show you random things and ask you to identify them, and whatever you can't identify, we'll put on a list. Maybe we can come up with a theme and then a plan of action."

This is why I love this girl – she does anything to help me. She always has.

"Okay," I say getting up from the bed and enveloping her in a big hug. "See you then." I flash her a smile.

"Better to live one year as a tiger than a hundred as a sheep."

Madonna

CHAPTER 8
The Decision ♡

Somewhere during those never-ending days and nights, the 17th of October arrives. My birthday. I'm 36 now. A woman that had a stroke. In a hospital room, hooked up to machines and the IV needle that hasn't left my vein since I arrived. What a shitty way to spend a birthday.

I entertain myself a little with the idea of possible guests, and maybe even flowers. Indeed, some co-workers and my mom come to visit me, and so do Frank and the kids. They bring me beautiful flowers and balloons. It makes my day.

Dreams of celebrating at home the way we always do, on the actual birthday with immediate family only, dance in my head, offering a temporary respite from the depressing atmosphere of my hospital room.

Exactly a year ago, Jowita and I were in Las Vegas celebrating together in style, since our birthdays are a mere three weeks apart. We stayed at the palatial Venetian hotel, splurged on the most exquisitely expensive food in Sin City, flew over the Hoover Dam and took boat rides on the Colorado river and helicopter tours of the Grand Canyon. All that feels like hundreds of years ago, and yet a short year later I'm hospitalized after a stroke, of all things, wondering whether I'm going to die in this place. How quickly life can change.

Having people visit me is my greatest joy while I'm serving my sentence in the hospital. Mom has visited me many times, co-workers, and of course my friends and Frank with the boys. I don't like the kids seeing me this way. I keep telling Frank not to bring them but I do miss them and they want to see me as well. They need to see me; they need that reassurance that I'm okay. I need reassurance too. More than anything I want to hear that I'm going to be fine and that I'll get through this. I want the doctors to confirm it. I need them to say it. But they don't.

The whole energy of this place is all about sickness, rushing and unkindness. It's a place of business. The nurses are there to work. So are the doctors. Offering reassurance and compassion is not part of their job description, so it's rarely done. The constant moaning and groaning, plus all the complaints coming from the other patients just fuel my fear and reinforce the idea that you're here to stay.

On the flip side, the positive thing about being in the hospital and spending so much time alone, with no access to the distraction of TV, radio, magazines, social media and the like, is that I'm able to really connect with myself and be fully present with my thoughts, therefore I can be fully aware of how this whole experience is affecting me.

As I watch each day's final visitor walk away, returning to their normal life, I'm reminded that I'm back to another miserable night, with my loyal companions – loneliness and fear. They are religiously fed by the loud PA announcements, beeping machines and innumerable nurses fussing around me but barely acknowledging my presence.

A vision

Another night, as Jowi leaves, depressing feelings set in.

"What day is today?" I wonder. I wish I'd asked her. Since she came in the evening and after work, it must be a weekday, though I can't be sure. I wouldn't put it past that girl to go to the office on the weekend.

If I'm lucky, I'll be able to rest a little. I turn off the light, climb in bed and pull the blankets all the way up to my chin. This place is so damn cold. *"Of course, they keep dead bodies in this place too,"* I remind myself. I shudder at the thought, a cold chill going up my spine. Dead people freak me out. The look of their lifeless and grotesque body makes my skin crawl. This is something that has been with me since about the age of 5 when I was forced to say goodbye to my deceased paternal grandfather after cancer claimed his life. *"This place is where sick people come, many of whom come to die,"* I continue. *"They have a morgue in this building because people die here, remember?"* Here I go again with these kinds of thoughts.

These thoughts love to travel in packs. Once one comes, their friends rush to be with them. *"I wonder if the morgue is close."*

Ego jumps in. *"Oh hell no Simone. No one is ready to die, okay? And who the fuck cares about where the morgue is?"*

"Of course not," I retort. *"I'm definitely **not** ready to die. There's lots I want to do."*

"And just so you know, I care, okay? I don't want to be near dead people," I add, completely annoyed.

I take a deep breath, taking in the clinical hospital air and the chlorinated scent of the sheets and blankets.

I shift my attention to the list of things I want to do in my life, things that make me forget my present depressing situation and dream of a beautiful future, like:

1. Quit my soul-sucking government job when I get out of here,

2. Teach people all about working out,

3. Write books,

4. Do fitness competitions,

5. Watch my boys grow and have kids of their own,

6. Start life on my own, as a single woman and mom.

I have no time for illness or death. I literally have no time to be sick or to die. Staring at the ceiling, the beeping machines serenading me in the background, I come to a sudden realization – that being in the hospital is actually keeping me from getting started on that list.

"Damn it, I wish I knew what the statistics are about how many people die in hospitals," I wonder. *"Would the nurse tell me? Probably not."* I convince myself. But I have to know. I'm becoming obsessed with this thought.

"I officially want you guys to know that I refuse to be death's victim," I tell Ego and Inner Me empowered. *"I hate this place. I want to go home. What's the point of being here all alone when I could be all alone in the comfort of my home?"*

"Oh yes," says Ego. *"You should definitely go home. Take a nice bath and get in that comfortable bed, watch some TV, read...."*

Ego definitely knows how to entice me and has always done such a great job of it. I really do miss my amazing, comfortable, king size bed. And my room. In fact, I miss my entire house. I miss cooking in my kitchen. I miss my large bathtub and taking relaxing baths by candlelight. I miss my couch too. I never sat on it that much, but right about now, I bet I'd be so much more comfortable on the couch than in this damn hospital bed. What's there to like here?

It surely feels like I've been in the hospital for what seems like centuries...in fact, lifetimes. I feel like I've been kept in maximum security jail, eating shitty food and letting my muscles go to waste.

I'm so, so tired. Emotionally and physically. Tired of these procedures with their constant blood draws, scans, tests, inspections and more tests. Today, they tell me that I have to be on this damn medication for the rest of my life to prevent another stroke from happening. How depressing. I need pills to stay alive. Further confirmation that I'm not okay.

And honestly, I'm really not okay. Mostly and especially mentally. It takes all my effort every single day to keep going. The sad, gloomy tone and energy of this place is indescribable. I feel like I'm about to lose something valuable, but I'm not ready to give up my sanity...my very self.

To say that everything is frustrating is a gross understatement. Doctors come and go, mostly for tests, using medical jargon I can't understand. Nurses poke and prod me without my consent, as if I've volunteered for medical research. And the food, if you can even call it that, is not fit for human consumption. It's so horrendous that I would only feed it to someone I was trying to poison.

"Wait, if something should happen while you're home alone, who would even know?" interjects Inner Me.

"Don't go instilling fear now," snaps Ego.

"Well she's right," I say. *"If something happens while I'm all alone and let's assume I die, no one will know until someone finds my body."*

AGAINST MEDICAL ADVICE

I shake my head at the visual of my dead body being found by Frank. Or worse, my kids.

*"Ummmm, you said you're **definitely** not ready to die. That you refuse to be death's victim. Those were your exact words,"* Ego says sarcastically.

"I'm not. And I assure you, I won't," I reply, equally sarcastic.

Both Inner Me and Ego know I'm not kidding. They both know that when I want something, wild horses can't hold me back from getting it.

It's the night I reach saturation level with this hellhole. I'm sure all these horrendous thoughts of death and dying have something to do with it.

"Okay, fuck!!! I can't do this anymore!!! I gotta get out of here." I tell Ego and Inner Me. *"I can't take even one more minute of this fucking bullshit!!!! If they don't think I'm going to get better and I need some damn pills to stay alive, then what's the fucking point of staying here?"*

The Escape

And in that moment, something was born. A decision. A beautiful conclusion...a resolution to my plight. Decisions are typically made after careful consideration. No consideration needed here. The writing was in plain sight, on the wall: I hate being here. **I absolutely hate this**. I hate what they do to me, like I'm a lab rat. I hate their reinforcement of doom and gloom and risk and all the other bullshit. I am **done** with it all. **I am going home!!! Tonight!! Now!!**

After I give birth to that glorious decision, I get this incredibly powerful surge of energy. Out of nowhere. I have no idea why or how or where the energy came from, but I feel so empowered, like I have all the power in the world available to me, to use as I see fit. I am

120

omnipotent...Godlike. I'm not going home to die. No matter what it takes, I'm going to be perfectly okay, go on, and thrive. I'm going to stand on my own two feet, look life in the eyes, and tell it that if it was trying to kill me, it can't fucking kill **me**. I am the child of two of the strongest people alive after all.

"I am going home!" I announce loudly and triumphantly to Inner Me and Ego.

"Yeeeeessssss," rejoices Ego. *"That's my girl. And don't worry, I'm here for you and we'll do this together,"* he adds. *"No matter what happens, we got this."*

"Are you sure?" asks Inner Me, calm as always.

"Do I ever do things when I'm unsure?"

"Well, you haven't been here long. And your speech...".

"I wasn't planning to be here long to begin with," I respond, annoyed.

"And look, I have the most important things I need right? I have you guys, I'm mobile, I have the ability to think and make decisions. That's a pretty strong foundation, wouldn't you say? I know what you're going to say, but Anna was in a coma and on life support," I remind Inner Me about Frank's mom. *"If I was in that state, I'd be worried, but I'm not, so, let's do this,"* I say, with purpose in my tone.

The morning lightning struck, it was just a regular day to me and I was just having a terrible headache, that's all. I still went on and rode my motorcycle, went to the gym, to Max's and back home, then to Frank's and back home, threw a party, celebrated Thanksgiving and my birthday, and saw my kids off to school, too. All that despite the horrendous headache. Things were planned and needed to be done. I always keep my word and when I say I'm going to do something, I do it – no ifs, ands, or buts.

All that and I didn't die. And leaving the hospital to go home, relax, rest and be comfortable was going to kill me? **Come on.**

Sure, it's crazy to go home and be all alone so soon, but hey, I'd already been through so much in life – the stroke, almost being abducted, almost drowning, and two human beings coming out of my body. Miracles happen every damn day and miracles are waiting to be made every single day. In fact, I'm ready to go home and get started on creating more miracles. I'm ready to become a different person, one that reaches new levels of resiliency. No more being scared, no more being a guinea pig and a science experiment for the doctors.

I feel so empowered! The decision I just made reminds me of how badass I am. How does Inner Me not know this? She keeps wanting me to be soft and cautious. There's no damn way I can be soft. Soft doesn't exist in my world. Except for ice cream. Ice cream is soft. But how long does ice cream last? It melts when exposed to heat. Inner Me is so wise, how does she not know these things? And **cautious??? Me?? Really???**

I'm done being mediocre, vulnerable and afraid! This is just a medical thing. But I didn't die, so I'm okay. My dad taught me that the only time you lose everything – including your ability to rebuild – is when you lose your life. So since I still have my life, I have all I need to rebuild. I'm ready to go to the next level, to make shit happen. I'm ready to buckle down and heal myself, focus on getting back to 100% and start the next chapter of my life as a single woman. Oh yes, I am ready. I **know** that I'm capable of doing amazing things, and I can't wait even another minute to set the wheels in motion to start that new chapter.

I throw the covers off and get up from the hospital bed, with renewed energy coursing through me. I turn on the light and push the button that calls the nurse, then sit back to wait, full of excitement.

"Please remind me to look up that aphasia term again when I get home. Oh and the stats about how many people die in hospitals," I instruct Inner Me and Ego.

"You got it baby," Ego replies full of excitement.

"And I'll likely need help to make sure my sentences are correct, okay?"

That's the thing about this damn stroke, it has me trapped inside my mind, where I'm okay, healthy, lucid and perfectly normal. I'm thankful for the medical personnel taking care of me, providing me with a diagnosis, but now I wish they would leave me alone so that my body can heal, and I'll be perfectly fine. As long as I'm alive and my mind is at 100%, everything, and I mean **everything**, will be fine.

I see the nurse approaching. She picks up my chart and gives it a quick scan.

"Hello, Simone," she says as she inspects the IV bag, not even looking at me.

"Hello," I respond as sweetly as I can muster, then blurt out, "I want to go home."

Shocked, she turns around to look at me, then lets out a laugh, with an obvious twinge of pity. I'm quite sure she thinks I'm crazy for presenting this preposterous idea.

"Oh dear, you're not ready to go home," she replies, more pity in her voice. "Not for a while."

"Oh, I know," I say. "But I need to go home tonight." She looks at me like I **am** crazy.

"You're not medically cleared to go home just yet," she says, her tone getting firm.

"I know," I assure her. I do know very well that I would not be cleared to go home, but then again, I wouldn't have been cleared to ride a motorcycle after having a stroke either. Or drink alcohol. Or have a party. But I did all those and here I am. I'm annoyed at how cautious **she** is. I'm actually **really** annoyed right now at how they all underestimate the body's strength and the mind's ability to find what the body needs to heal.

"I'd like to sign myself out, please," I say sweetly.

"Against medical advice?" she asks, both shocked and annoyed now.

How dare I even think such a thing? Much less suggest it.

"Against medical advice," I respond with a smile, nodding.

"At this time of night?" she adds, her eyebrows shooting up.

"Yes."

She may not know it yet, but I'm going home, come hell or high water. Unless they tie me to the bed, I'm going home. This would not be the first time I ran away from the hospital after being admitted.

"Did you already arrange to have someone pick you up?" she asks, squinting her eyes suspiciously. By now she's thinking that I've planned this whole escape. Which I did. In the last five minutes.

"My husband," I lie.

I'm sure that if she found out that I'll be home alone, she'd order security guards at my door and escort me to the bathroom, all to ensure I don't take off.

"Is he here?" she asks, looking around. Now she's mocking me.

"He's on his way," I answer, smiling.

"I'll let the doctor know you want to go home, but I can tell you right now, no one in this hospital would approve of you leaving tonight," she replies, annoyance very obvious in her voice. She walks away.

As soon as she's gone, I reach into the bottom drawer of the nightstand and pull out my bag. My husband had been kind enough to bring me clean clothes.

I put on my underwear and yoga pants. My shirt has to wait until she comes back to remove the IV from my arm.

I sit on the bed, full of excitement. I'm going home. Tonight I'll sleep in my very own, super comfortable, king size bed. I'll also take a nice, long, relaxing shower. Back to my life, with a new lease. I can hardly wait.

I realize that I told the nurse that my husband is coming to pick me up. I haven't even told him I'm leaving the hospital.

Thank God I have a phone in my room since my cell was left home when I was brought to the hospital. I pick up and slowly dial his number, silently praying that he'll pick up. It's rare that he doesn't answer his phone, especially if I call, but since I'm calling from the hospital, he has no idea it's me. Hospital numbers don't show up on the caller ID.

"Hello?" he answers, sounding half asleep.

"Hi," I say cheerfully, full of energy, as if it's the middle of the day.

"Simone, hi. You okay?" He asks. He sounds more awake now and full of concern.

"I'm fine," I reassure him, my voice confident and excited. "I'm coming home. Please come get me."

"Now?" he asks shocked.

"Yes, please."

"Okay, I'll be there in ten minutes," he says.

That's the thing I always loved about Frank. He did anything for me, no matter how crazy my request. He once drove for two hours in a blizzard from hell in the dead of winter because I needed to buy a pair of boots that were only available at a particular location. Love really is expressed in many many different ways.

"Thank you so much. See you soon," I say, full of happiness.

I hang up and dump the bag of clean clothes on the bed so I can find a shirt suitable for the weather. *"I wonder what the weather is like,"* I think to myself. A split second later, visions of taking a nice hot bath and sleeping in my own bed whisk me off to a faraway land of all the great things I'll be able to do again very soon. I'm so caught up in my daydream that I don't hear the nurse and the doctor when they come back in.

"What is this I hear about you wanting to go home tonight, young lady?" the doctor asks, peering at me over glasses perched low on his nose. His look is piercing, almost menacing. He scans the chart, his eyes darting all over the page and back at me, waiting for me to answer. I jump, startled by his voice.

"Yes, I want to go home," I respond confidently.

In my mind, this is already a done deal, it has already come true, already happened. It's just a matter of time before it's expressed in physical reality.

"And why is that?" he questions me, his piercing look probing for an answer.

"So I can rest and relax and get better. And be with my family," I respond, smiling.

I can already tell that he's not even considering allowing me to leave, but it doesn't matter. I'm leaving anyway. I'm also within my rights to sign myself out of my own volition. Back when I was 10 years old and hospitalized in Romania, I ran away because I was too young to sign myself out.

I cannot even fathom being stuck in this depressing place for another minute with no access to light or fresh air. Who in their right mind wants to stay here willingly? Not me.

"Well you're not okay to go home just yet," he says, still looking at my chart.

"I'm okay to go home. I want to get a good night's sleep," I say, feelings of annoyance starting to creep into my voice. "I'm obviously okay, I'm not bedbound," I add defiantly, amazed that I have to even state the obvious.

What these people don't know is that I am not okay with being told what to do and being kept somewhere against my will. If I was not okay with being forced to stay in a hospital at 10, you can bet that I will not be okay with it at 36.

"Please don't let me mess up my sentences," I pray. I don't want to give them ammunition so they can justify keeping me here.

"I'll assume the risk and sign off on things," I say, looking right at him.

"Atta girl," says Ego with the utmost pride.

Smiling, I turn to the nurse. "Could you please take this out?" I say, holding out my arm with the IV needle. She turns to the doctor, a perplexed look on her face. He doesn't give her any direction so she doesn't move.

"Let's sit down and talk," the doctor says, motioning towards the bed. "You're not out of the woods just yet. You're at high risk for another stroke right now, because you just had one. It's best that you are here where you can get the help you need right away, so you can get better," he says.

"I see," I say, not convinced. He's insane. And what's the deal with this "you just had one"? He makes it sound like I had one in the last ten minutes. Ugh. And he's speaking to me like I'm a child. My mother spoke to me in that simplistic language when she was trying to entice me to eat or drink something that tasted horrible. She would try to sell me with the "so you can get better" bullshit too.

I'm still going home. That's the thing about me – when I've made my mind up about something, it's very hard to keep me from following through.

"Please don't let me mess up my sentences," I pray again.

"Is another stroke guaranteed to happen?" I ask him calmly.

"You are brilliant," announces Ego. *"So brilliant."*

"Well, no, it's not a guarantee but the risk is there and it's high, so it can definitely happen," he answers.

I know this and he's technically right. My mother-in-law had multiple successive strokes before dying. But she was in a coma following her first stroke. She was also significantly older, heavier and a smoker.

Why doctors assume that I would follow the same path as other patients is beyond me. At this point I feel anger rising within me.

"Is this doctor certified to be a doctor?" Ego wonders.

He reminds me of a doctor long, long ago – when I was a mere teenager – who maintained that my father was a heavy drinker because his test results were similar to those of an alcoholic with severe liver damage. My father always hated alcohol and only drank on occasions like birthdays, Christmas and New Year's Eve. This doctor stubbornly insisted that my father drank, as if he lived with us and actually saw my father drinking with his own eyes. The idea that non-alcoholic fatty liver disease could even be a medical possibility was so foreign to this doctor that he tried to convince my father and me (I was at that appointment with my dad) that we were both lying to ourselves about my dad's drinking. This, despite the fact that he knew my father had an affinity for sweets, and since alcohol is also sugar, perhaps the sugar came from other sources. But why think further than what has been taught in school, right? Why use common sense?

This is precisely why I always despised allopathic medicine. Everyone is treated the same if they suffer from the same thing. But every human body is not the same. How is it that doctors have not been taught this fact? Medicine and science have surely advanced enough to have at least uncovered the biochemical uniqueness of every body. The uniqueness of the fingerprint should've given them a hint.

I am 36 years old, fit, with a clean lifestyle and no history of cardiovascular issues that would put me at risk of stroke. I'm also the first person on both the maternal and paternal sides of my family to have a stroke. How does he reason that I'm at risk of a subsequent stroke? And if he can substantiate his claim, why does he not share it with me? Why am I always kept in the dark and expected to just accept what is being said and done to me?

Why does he not even acknowledge that there's also a big chance that I would be just fine, that my brain would heal and that I would thrive and be perfectly fine?

"But there's also a big chance that I'll be just fine, right?" I ask him.

"Well, yes of course," he answers hesitantly.

"Great," I say, full of energy. "That's exactly what I plan to do – be just fine, heal and move on with my life and make it amazing," I add, flashing him my biggest smile. "Where do I sign so I can go home?" I stand up and extend my arm toward the nurse again. "Could you please?"

She looks at the doctor, unsure of how to proceed. He doesn't even acknowledge her.

"Young lady, let me remind you, you are not cleared to go anywhere," he says sternly. "Get some rest," he says as he stands up and starts walking away, the nurse close behind him.

Catching Ego's anger rising I say, *"Be cool. Don't worry, we're doing this. We're escaping. Trust me."*

"Oh hell yes we will," he rejoices, replacing his anger with excitement.

I can't even recall the last time I felt this happy, this ecstatic, this elated. I feel like I'm about to escape from Alcatraz. In my mind, I'm the female version of Frank Morris – one of only three inmates to escape from the notorious prison, where the infamous gangster Al Capone was also a prisoner. When a decision is made and I'm ready to move on it, it's like tasting the sweetness of life.

Ego is doing back-flips. *"Yessss! Let's blow this popsicle stand,"* he says triumphantly.

Both the doctor and the nurse are safely out of the room.

Escape! My heart is racing from the excitement. I decide to pull out the IV needle myself. I've seen this done a million times. How hard can it be? I grab a tissue from the box on the nightstand, peel off the tape covering the IV needle, pull the needle out of my vein and quickly apply pressure with the tissue.

When I'm done I phone Frank again. He picks up after the first ring.

"Are you far?" I ask. I'm so eager to get out of here that I don't even greet him.

"I just parked," he responds. "Are you in the same room?"

"Yes."

"Okay, see you in a few."

"Okay, bye." I hang up, practically levitating. My heart is racing and I have butterflies in my stomach. This is about to happen.

A few minutes later, Frank enters the room, holding two large cups from Tim Hortons.

"I got you your favorite tea," he says, handing me a cup.

"Pumpkin Spice?" I ask excitedly.

"Of course."

I'm very impressed. He always had a terrible memory and I had a lot of favorite teas – chamomile, mint, sencha green tea, and of course pumpkin spice in the fall.

Little do I know in this moment that love is shown through small things and gestures every single day. He definitely showed his love for me more times than I can count.

"So how come they're letting you out at this time of night? I would've thought that they'd release you during the day," he says.

I hate lying but this calls for it.

"Weeeellll, I asked to go home," I say, taking a small sip of the tea. I know there's caffeine in this tea and I shouldn't be drinking it if I want to sleep tonight, but I know that I can sleep in tomorrow. "Is that really a good idea, Simone?" he asks, concerned. "Having a stroke isn't like having a cold, it's serious," he adds.

I understand his concerns. I can't even imagine what it would do to him to lose me the same way the way he lost his mom.

"Oh, I'll be fine," I say and walk over to him. "You know I'm a fighter. I push through things. I'll be okay, I promise." I put my cup on the nightstand and give him a hug. "Thank you for coming to get me," I say.

"Of course," he answers and holds me close. In that moment the awkwardness is gone and we're momentarily back to being okay, happily married and in love. Maybe it's my excitement and happiness, maybe it's his fear that I may die like his mother, maybe it's a sign from heaven...who knows?

"I can't wait to take a shower," I tell him and start to laugh. "And get some real sleep," I add, my voice full of giddiness.

The nurse walks in. Her spectacles are low on her nose.

"Hello, are you the husband?" she asks, looking at him above her glasses.

"Yes, I am," he replies.

"I'm sure you know that Simone wants to leave against medical advice." She clearly wants to make sure he knows I'm not medically cleared to go home.

"Perfect sentences, please," I silently pray again.

"Oh, he knows," I jump in to respond. She doesn't know it, but I'm about to escape regardless of medical advice.

Thank God I'm standing next to the IV pole. I hope she doesn't realize the needle is no longer in my arm.

She's busy writing something down on my chart.

"It's past visiting hours," she says looking at me. "And you need rest."

"Is she for real?" I think to myself. *"Has she ever tried to fucking **rest** in this place?"*

What's wrong with these hospital people? Why are they treating me like I'm an obese smoker who wants to go home so I can eat fried egg sandwiches on donuts with a pile of bacon while playing games on my iPad or watching TV?

I am so pumped to start anew – to go back to school, to read, to meditate, do yoga, run again, and give thanks to God every day for giving me another chance at this thing we call life.

"So get some rest," she says sternly, looking right at me before she leaves the room. Little does she know that I never play to lose, I always play to win. And I always win. Tonight, I am sleeping in my bed. This is a fact.

As soon as she's gone, I grab the bag of clothes and head to the bathroom to finish getting dressed. When I'm ready, I step out and say triumphantly to Frank, "Let's go home." I want to get out quickly, before she has a chance to come back, see me gone and announce code yellow (for missing patient) over the PA system.

"But she said ...."

"Come on," I say, pulling him towards the door.

Luckily, my room is at the end of the hallway, near the entrance to the stroke patient area. Being far away from the nurse's station is a blessing. Proof that God had planned to help me escape long before it even entered my mind.

I stab at the elevator button impatiently. It feels like a lifetime before the elevator arrives, and another few lifetimes for the doors to open. I press the G button over and over with childlike giddiness. A million lifetimes later we get to the ground floor.

Out of the elevator, I can almost taste the freedom I was yearning for. I see the revolving door leading outside. I pick up the pace, walking towards the exit as if trying to elude the police. In my mind, I'm escaping from prison.

As I step outside, my new life begins. I breathe in the cold, crisp air. I've never enjoyed breathing as much as I do in that moment and I couldn't be more excited if I tried. Or feel any more free.

"*You don't have to know how it's going to happen, you just have to know that it's going to happen.*"

Bob Proctor

CHAPTER 9

Fighting my Paradigms ♡

I'm **home**! What a joy! I stand in the cold air, looking at my house, and a thought flashes in my mind. *"I've always taken this for granted,"* I think, and all of a sudden I feel this huge wave of gratitude for having a house to go to.

Entering the house, I'm hit with mixed emotions. Yes, I had a stroke in here. But this is my home. I'm back home. I can be here with my kids. I'm free. It's quiet. I can take a shower. I can sleep in my own bed. And this is exactly what I'm going to do. Frank makes his way to the living room.

Slowly, I go upstairs, appreciating every step, every color, every view, every artwork on the wall, every piece of furniture, the carpets on the floor. I open the door to Marcus's room and see my little angel sleeping peacefully, the blanket up to his chin. I kneel down by his bed and caress him taking in the beauty of the moment. "I love you my baby" I whisper and kiss his head. I walk a few feet to Roman's room and see his little body sprawled on his bed, his teddy-bear safe in his arms. I sit on the side of the bed and pull the blanket to cover him and his teddy. A rush of gratitude envelops me. "I love you so much my little baby." I whisper looking at him.

"Thank you for keeping them safe," I add looking up at the ceiling.

I kiss Roman's cheek lightly and walk quietly out of the room.

Just being able to be near my boys again is the greatest and most divine gift this day has brought.

As soon as I get to the master bedroom, I undress and throw the clothes in the trash can, to erase any memory from the hospital, from that horribleness that felt like imprisonment.

Then, I thoroughly enjoy my shower. I enjoy the sensation of warm water on my skin. The familiar fragrance of my organic soap brings me back to the days of my routine and to the days when Frank and I were happily married and raising our kids. I touch the wall, and kiss it. I chose those tiles. I love them so much right now. I'm so thankful to be home that it overwhelms me and I burst into tears. I stand there sobbing as the water washes over me, cleansing me, the tears releasing all the pent-up emotions of fear. I feel so incredibly relieved.

"You're amazing, Simone," says Ego. This is the first time he sounds soft and kind. *"You're doing so amazing,"* he continues.

"And you are more beautiful than you even know," adds Inner Me.

"I love you guys! What would I do without you?" I respond between sobs.

I stand there crying for what seems like an eternity, in a new world, as a new me, in a new life, with a new future ahead of me. I'm sad that I became a statistic of stroke on top of a statistic of divorce, but I'm also seriously excited about all the possibilities that lie ahead. I have no idea how it will all unfold, but the how doesn't even really matter. The only thing that matters is that it's happening – I am alive and my new life, not just as a divorced woman, but as a woman who had a stroke, has begun.

I go back to that fateful Saturday and how everything changed in a mere nanosecond. The lightning strike in my head forever changed me and my whole being, forever changed my views, forever changed my life. I see myself on the floor, vulnerable, completely stripped down, devoid of all the human bullshit. I see myself in the busy hospital, curled on the stretcher in the hallway filled with the hospital noise, harried EMS medics bringing in people to be treated. I feel sorry for myself, seeing myself like that. It was lonely. That was the moment I needed someone more than ever. I was at my absolute lowest ever. Then tonight, the night I escaped....I feel the emotion of excitement again and let out a triumphant laugh through the tears, as the water is still pouring over me from above. Pride takes over the feeling of excitement. I realize just how many things I was able to do through this entire ordeal. Immediately after the stroke, I pushed my body past the limits of the medical frontiers.

If only I knew then that the world's most brutal headache was my body screaming at me, trying to get my attention.

"I'm sorry I didn't listen to you," I say to Inner Me.

"It's okay," she says softly. *"I love you and always will. And I'll always be with you."*

I fast forward to Tuesday morning when I attempted to put the wine glasses back in the credenza. Exhausted, spent and probably fed up, I'm sure my body said, *"Okay, Simone, **enough**!!!"* I see myself crumpled on the floor. I should've known that eventually that's what the body would do. Each time I had been sick in the past, without fail, the body forced me to get out of the way and let it do its healing work in peace, unobstructed and uninterrupted, whether it was by turning up the core temperature to kill whatever invader was lurking inside, by shutting down my appetite and by forcing me to sleep.

"I'm sorry my amazing body" I say, my voice full of deep regret. *"I won't do that again,"* I promise. *"I'm so grateful for all you do for me. You are so magnificent and so resilient. Thank you!"*

The cool water brings me back to reality, all the hot water having run out.

I turn off the faucet and kiss the wall again, then step out and look around. Everything is exactly as I had left it, untouched.

In my jammies, I sit on my bed and look at my room with a new sense of appreciation. I never thought being home would feel so good. My regal four poster bed, the beautiful Romanesque artwork on the wall, the flat TV, the luxurious duvet, pillows, curtains, the nightstands, the lamps and the walk-in closet. My bedroom. My bed. Neatly made as usual – my first achievement of the day. Always. I sit on the side I'm used to sleeping on and then throw myself on my back. *"Oh my God, this is the best thing since mankind was created,"* I say to myself.

The feeling of almost losing all this...and now I have it all back. As I lie there like a starfish, I feel how good it is to be back at home. I feel grateful and empowered, happy and so proud of myself.

My room smells so nice. Nothing clinically sterile. My good-looking, feel-good pillows. So many gorgeous things I've never appreciated. All my clothes, my shoes – everything! Even my bathroom. My big bathroom with the huge tub and the separate all-glass shower is a far cry from the miniscule hospital bathroom with a toilet that didn't even have a cover. I had lived in sheer luxury that Frank and I worked so hard to get and was completely unappreciative of it. I had come a long way from the deficits of my life in Communist Romania where luxury was unattainable to most. And kept my promise to myself to never live like that again, at the hand of the government. It was time to be proud of my achievements and the life I had created for myself and my family.

I'm exhausted but ecstatically happy to be back. With those relaxing and calming thoughts in my mind, I climb in bed and rest my head on the pillows, duvet under my chin. It's almost 1:00 am. I turn on the sound machine and quickly fall into a deep, peaceful sleep. It's the best sleep I have in decades.

The morning

When I wake up, it's daylight outside. It takes me a few seconds to realize that I truly am back home. And that sense of gratitude embraces me again. Oh my God, I'm home. I can't wait to have breakfast in my kitchen again. I can't wait to see the kids and to go outside in the backyard with Bella.

A glance at my phone tells me it's 11:00 am. I've slept ten hours without waking up even to pee! My usual sleeping time is seven or eight hours. I feel so good now. I was definitely exhausted. I hadn't had a full night's deep restful sleep since I entered the hospital. Not even one.

Flowing with gratitude, I walk down the stairs. My house looks so good. There must be someone watching over me. There is someone watching over me. *"Maybe it's mamaia,"* I think, referring to my grandmother who died back home. I never said a proper goodbye to her and to this day I miss her. She was an angel in human form when I was growing up. *"Or maybe it's Anna."* I think of Frank's mom, who was always on a par with my mom as one of the world's greatest cooks.

Looking around my house, I have a true mindfulness moment. A first glimpse of the avalanche of the spiritual awakening ahead of me.

The home phone rings. Oh, the sweet sounds of the home phone. I answer it without even checking to see who's calling. I wish I had. I would've figured by the "Private

Caller" that appeared on the caller ID screen that it was the hospital.

"Hello?" I say, feeling gratitude that I'm able to do even a small thing like answer the phone.

"May I speak with Simone Gisondi?" asks the woman on the other end. Whoever she is, she's very upset. I can tell by the tone of her voice.

"This is she," I respond.

She proceeds to scold me and remind me that I was irresponsible for leaving and instructs me to go back to the hospital.

She is insane. The only way I would voluntarily go back there is if a loved one was there. Under absolutely no other circumstances would I even consider the idea.

What prisoner would willingly go back to Alcatraz?

I give her the benefit of the doubt. She doesn't know how I feel about this whole thing. She doesn't know that I don't live in the fear she's trying to project onto me.

"Be kind," Inner Me says.

A doctor takes over.

"Mrs. Gisondi," he says sternly, completely botching my last name. It's clear that this is not going to be a two-way conversation. It affirms why I left. "You left the hospital against a doctor's advice. You clearly don't understand how serious a stroke is. Strokes kill." I feel like a child being scolded by an angry father.

How annoying. Don't they understand anything? Do they ever give a thought to how the patient feels about things?

"Be kind," Inner Me repeats. She must've felt the impatience rising up inside me.

I keep my cool and let him ramble on.

In the end I reluctantly agree to go for follow-up appointments.

I'm not fully committed to doing it but I verbally agree.

"You are such an idiot! An educated fool," I say out loud when I hang up. *Can you guys believe these people? They have no idea what I need so I can heal. They don't know me as a person; they didn't even care to get to know me or at least ask me what I need. They know me as a number with a barcode and a name. And they have the audacity to give me shit because I want to heal myself **my** way! Like I'm their property! Can you believe this? Don't they fucking know that God can help in ways no doctor or hospital ever can? Ugh!* I tell Inner Me and Ego. *"Have they ever heard of spontaneous healings?"*

I never gave deeper thought to this, but these people don't realize that not everybody heals the same way. That health is not a conveyor belt where patients are carbon copies of each other, and you give them the same medication and the same protocol. It doesn't work like that.

Some people embrace that victim mentality, probably love being in the hospital, because all these people are paying attention to them. They come and they do things for you. And they give you what they think you need, so you don't need to think, since your health and your life are completely in their hands. You have absolutely no responsibility whatsoever. I guess it must feel good to have that kind of attention, where other people's job is to focus on you and administer to you what they were taught in school by people that never asked **anyone** what they need, as a unique individual, to heal.

But me, I can't stand the victim mentality. I was always taught to take responsibility for everything. My parents accepted nothing less. Being a victim always equaled being weak to me. And who has time to sit in the same spot feeling sorry for themselves because something happened to them? Throughout my life I always had something ahead of me that I wanted to do, so I never had time to wallow in my misfortunes. I would push forward and try to achieve something or other.

New routines

Now that I'm back home, I'm alone a lot while the boys are at school and on the weekends when they're at Frank's. I don't feel lonely like I did in the hospital. Now, I really love my alone time. Whereas before I wanted to be surrounded by people, now solitude is a divine gift.

Healing is my number one priority. I'm not sure what I actually need to heal my brain or how I'm going to achieve it, but I know with certainty that I am at peace being back home and the peace feels really good. I also know that their method – the hospital method – doesn't work for me. This I am 100% certain of. I find out later that the stress I was under in that hospital was contributing to my inability to get better and increasing my risk of illness. Stress contributes to 99% of all illnesses after all.

I have a lot of time on my hands. I start journaling because I feel the urge to write, to reflect and pour my feelings out. And it does feel good. I always loved to write. I got into the habit of it back when I was a kid and wanted to invent magical worlds like the ones I read about in children's books. I did a writing assignment in high school English that I was elated about, one that I looked forward to working on. I should have carried on with writing, as that assignment earned me a nice mark, which shocked me. I was an immigrant, after all, and English wasn't my first language. Now, writing down ten things to be grateful for daily makes me not just appreciate things I have, but also my life and the things that happened, even the stroke itself. *"My God, I was such a spoiled brat. Kudos to Frank for putting up with me,"* I think one morning after going through the routine which fed my soul…journaling, being in the moment as I made breakfast for me and the boys, getting them ready for school and talking to my mom, something I still do daily even all these years later.

Without the stroke, I probably would've never appreciated everything I have. I accumulated stuff, I worked hard to have those things, but I never really took the time to actually enjoy and be grateful for them.

One day, after dropping the kids off at Frank's, I stop at a used bookstore on a whim and an intuition. Four dollars later I walk out with what would become my bible, Louise Hay's book "You Can Heal Your Life". Jowita had told me about this book.

I'm grateful for all the information that comes my way, although not every piece of it enchants me, especially stroke survivors' stories and those of their loved ones. Not all of them have a happy ending, but there's one thing in common – the way stroke is treated medically. I'm past the shock and anger at this point, but I do wonder why medical professionals don't ever ask the patient, "What do you need to feel better?"

Gratitude is my tool for inner peace. I start to meditate, and I also pray. I did it before, too, but now I'm sure more than ever that God is with me every moment of every day. I no longer ask for things, but rather I say thanks for them, because I'm am now aware that I had them all along.

One night, in my highly-appreciated regal bed, I decide to have a candid conversation with God.

"I know now that you had my back all along and always will. Thank you so much for always blessing me and continuing to even when I was acting so spoiled and entitled. But I do have a request tonight, God. It's something I've always wanted. Could you show yourself to me somehow? I want to see what you look like." I lay there in the dark and in silence, waiting. *"What could God actually look like?"* I wonder. Nothing happens. I fall asleep.

The next evening, Jowita comes to visit me. It's usually me that goes to her house for our weekly get togethers, but this time, she makes the drive to me. We sit on the couch, drinking tea and talking until the early hours of the morning, much like we do at her house. All of a sudden, I'm jolted by a feeling that I can't quite describe, but one that indicates that we're no longer alone. "Oh my God, somebody's here!" I blurt out. Out of the corner of my eye, to the right, I see three white lights moving around above us. That moment it hits me – God is here.

"What? What do you mean? Who's here?" asks Jowita, clearly freaked out a little by my announcement.

It's past 2:00 am so such a statement would certainly freak someone out. Had I been in her place, I probably would've been freaked out too.

A few minutes pass, the three lights are still moving about the room above and to the right.

Jowita decides to leave, though I don't know whether it's because of how late it is or because she's too weirded out to stay longer. I walk her to her car, hoping that the three lights would be waiting for me when I get back into the house so we can be alone. I fully intend to continue my chat with God.

"Oh wow, God, you came. Thank you for showing yourself," I say, so overwhelmed that fat tears spill from my eyes.

"Thank you for watching over me. Thank you for not letting me die. Thank you for the second chance. Thank you for giving my kids their mother back. Thank you for giving me another chance to continue being their mom. Thank you for all the great things that you've helped me accumulate in life. Thank you for everything I have. Thank you for all you're teaching me."

I feel no fear. I feel the trust. I feel alive. I'm accepting the unconditional love. Finally.

"If you must doubt something, doubt your limits."

Bob Proctor

CHAPTER 10

Breaking Free ♡

The first six months at home are an adventure. An emotional rollercoaster. The fear instilled in me by all the literature on stroke as well as the doctors and nurses I interacted with during my hospital stay is something I have to keep at bay each and every day. It's also what I have to erase from my mind.

Though I don't share this thought with anyone, deep inside I fear I'll never see 40. Each day I question why such a thought even enters my head. Inner Me reassures me that all is well, but this thought is so real, it even pushes itself into my mind when I meditate. I would pay any amount of money to anyone willing to extract it from my mind, like an abscessed tooth.

Week by week, my spirit is healing, and with that, so is my physical body. I have no desire to go back to the gym. Not just yet. The contrast is huge. Plus, I'm still on medications, and I'm sure the sleepiness is the side effect. Altogether I'm on three medications. I take them only because I'm told they help prevent more strokes, which of course I want to do. But why do I feel so horrible after I take them? I hate how I feel.

I hate taking them. The only time I feel peace is when I meditate, journal and read Louise's book.

What would happen if I were to stop taking them? The tingling on the left side of my body is gone but aphasia is still very much part of my life and occasionally I still have moments when I'm unable to articulate the words waiting patiently to be spoken.

At first, it's very stressful to buy myself time to run things by Inner Me so I can be sure that the sentences are correct and make perfect sense, but eventually I start calling those times when I can't articulate words my "stroke moments" and make fun of them. With this decision, embarrassment is slowly fading and being replaced with self-acceptance. A badge earned. I know I'm not stupid. The stroke has taken away the need to prove my well-developed brain to every single person. It has humbled me greatly.

The Struggle

I don't even believe the medications are working. I obediently do endless CT scans of my head to see if my brain is healing. And at every appointment they remind me that I'm at very high risk of having a second stroke given the fact that I had the first one, blah, blah, blah. Not something I want to hear. Instead of gaining hope, I feel like I'm robbed of it again. So, I'm struggling. A lot, and that makes the full physical recovery even harder. I hate the way medications still make me feel. I'm frustrated! Why do I have to take the same damn medications as all those elderly stroke patients?

Despite my greatest efforts to put it all behind me – the endless tests, the constant reminders about the risk of a second stroke, the medications – I spin into despair. All this, despite my meditations, journaling and self-care. I'm pulled in two different directions at the same time. I build myself up and gain new hope through my morning rituals, only to have everything crumble each time I interact with the medical world. A clash of two worlds. One I love, and one I had to escape from.

To say that I hate going to all the follow-up appointments and tests is a gross understatement. I feel like I go to hell to meet with the devil himself each time I go for an appointment. And he doesn't fail to remind me that I need the medical recommendations if I want to stay alive. Each appointment reminds me so much of how I felt when I was imprisoned in the hospital and how their recommendations led to all the side effects these medications have. I'm constantly reminded and led to believe that I need them – the meds and the appointments – yet it's just further attempts at instilling fear and the belief that I'm not okay. And to top it all off, medical people refer to me as a stroke survivor. Survivor. Ugh. I don't want to be known as that. I don't ever want to be known as a stroke anything! I'm not a victim of anything. The stroke did not victimize me. I'm... I'm Simone and I had a stroke!

It's not like the stroke was sent after me by someone or something, sent to kill me because I did something horrible to them. Oh no, far from it. It was me that created that stroke. It was all my doing. Every bit of it. That was my creation, so I'm appreciative of it at this point. I don't for one second feel anything negative towards the stroke, because it's done, it's gone, it's over with, it's part of a past that I am done with. I have let it go. It was merely an experience and it just so happens that not everyone can say they had this experience, that's all.

So why then? Why do they think it's okay to refer to me as a survivor? If someone breaks their leg you don't define them by that! You don't refer to them as a broken leg survivor. Okay, that might not be life-threatening, but let's take birth, for example, since many women have died while giving birth. We don't refer to the women who did NOT die as childbirth survivors, right? Because at that rate if we're going to call ourselves survivors of everything that we could've died from, I survived childbirth twice too.

Nobody talks like that! So why with stroke?

A stroke is just something that happened. It didn't even happen **to** me, it actually happened **for** me. It's not something that defines me and it's certainly not something that defines who or what I am. Things happen for everybody! Every day! It doesn't make them victims. I'm certainly not someone that was victimized by a disease that I decided to overcome. I don't ever look at myself as any of that! Nor will I ever. I don't want to take the energy of that into my future. I don't want an association with something I am done with. And I am done with the stroke. For good. And I assure you, there will **not** be another stroke.

When I go for my appointments, I meet people who glorify their diseases and wear their diagnoses like badges of honor. I think it's the pity some feel for me when they hear the S word that rubs against my self-worth the most. I don't deny that I had a stroke and I'm definitely not ashamed of it. It's simply something that happened during my life, and it definitely carries many positives that I am deeply grateful for. Sure, there are some negatives as well, but why even think about those? As far as I'm concerned, I'm doing all I can to go towards healing every single day. In every possible way. And negative things don't mix with healing.

I'm on a mission now. I look for alternatives but it takes me a while to understand what they are. To understand what I need the most to really heal, to understand what to eat so that I can support my body on its healing journey. Perhaps I need someone to tell me to go outside, to breathe in fresh air and enjoy sunshine, because moving your body outside helps you sleep better. Someone to explain the importance of mindset to me, how healing starts from our mind, and how everything around and within us is energy. Someone to encourage me and remind me that I'm young, athletic and healing every day because the body is naturally designed to do just that – heal. There's no one to tell me any of that. So I do it myself. I don't expect my loved ones to do the research for me. Everyone works, they all have their jobs. Yet, what they tell me is to take it easy. "Just take it easy."

Sure. I can do that. While I'm creating a whole new world for myself.

I increase the amount of time I spend researching. The rabbit hole is deep. How do you heal from a stroke? Who has healed and how? I was looking for success stories but couldn't really find many outside the medical world. I'm also ready to get my physical strength back; I'm ready to go back to the gym. *"Well then, you have to start eating like you're going back to the gym,"* I say to myself. And back to a structured diet I go.

Though I fear that I would have to rebuild from scratch in the gym, I know that my amazing muscles have memory and the neuromuscular system is waiting to help me. I had thought that maybe my stroke impacted the communication between the brain and the muscles, but it's really the nervous system that provides the link between thoughts and muscular actions. My nervous system is intact and ready, as are all my muscles.

So back to the gym I go, and I push forward with training, full steam ahead. Pound by pound and rep by rep I rebuild my stamina and strength while I reacquaint myself with all the machines and weights.

Though demons of fear are still lurking in the back of my mind, I make incredible strides, and ten months after my stroke I step on the fitness competition stage for the first time in my life and win. I am elated. And since I'm already stage ready, I do it again in October to celebrate my birthday and the year anniversary since my life changed forever.

The Difference

By the time I had the stroke, I had worked in healthcare for over ten years. The stroke was my first experience on the other side of the table, so to speak. I had never been a patient in this way. I had been a healthcare employee, on the business side, ensuring best practices for health services delivered to patients, never aware of what it would be like to actually be one. The difference is huge.

As an employee I had a voice. As a patient I did not; I was treated like an invalid with a disability, a case that needed medical help and a clinical approach, not a human being or a real person that needed compassion, kindness and a holistic approach to healing. The cookie cutter, generic protocol to treating stroke victims was applied as if hospitals are like mechanic shops, where all cars are the same – drain the oil, tighten the drain plug, change the oil filter and add the new oil. Next!

Medical treatment for stroke involves being stabilized and assessed as I was when the ambulance brought me in, and it's solely the doctors that develop a treatment plan for recovery.

Many, many tests are run. It's like a marathon of endless testing that's not only exhausting, but also detrimental to health. During my studies, I learn that computerized tomography scans (CT scans) emit powerful x-rays which are known to cause cancer. A CT scan typically exposes one to as much radiation as 200 chest x-rays. I had brain CT scans.

I also had to do magnetic resonance imaging (MRI), echocardiograms, carotid doppler, ECGs (electrocardiogram), EEGs (electroencephalogram) and interminable blood tests and tests to the left side of my body – grip strength, sensory motor performance, upper and lower limb functions, etc. etc. etc.

Fatigue and exhaustion are both very common after stroke. This is due to the damage sustained by the brain. It makes rest and relaxation that much more important for healing. The fatigue and exhaustion I experienced after my stroke was two pronged – body fatigue and brain fatigue. My body needed rest to heal itself, but it was impossible to sleep in the hospital. And let's not forget the side effects of medication on the body.

Then there's brain fatigue. A tired brain has trouble sorting out the things around it, like music, people talking, noise from the television, and bright lights. I was also swamped with feelings that cause fatigue – panic, anxiety, fear, helplessness. Those also affect the brain.

Most also feel more tired because of depression, something caused by the chemical imbalance in the brain. Stroke changes life in the blink of an eye, so naturally depression is common after stroke.

I decide I have no time for any of that. I'm too busy strategizing my life as a single woman to be depressed.

Fatigue can be a problem for several reasons. It may make some of your stroke symptoms seem worse. It may make you feel weaker and your speech more slurred. It can also make you more emotional than usual. I have no time for any of that either. I keep on studying. Fearlessly, I keep on rebuilding my life. With courage to live.

Yes, the silent fear of not knowing anything about what my future may hold is lodged deep in the recesses of my mind, but the joy of being healthy takes over. It feels beyond amazing. I feel truly alive.

The Shift

Fed up with the constant side effects of the medications I'd been prescribed, I abruptly stop taking the anticoagulants. The idea comes during meditation, and from Inner Me's guidance. She knew that there was a lot I could do all by myself to feel even better now that I was getting sleep, fresh air and movement. She instructs me to test how I would feel without all those chemicals that were prescribed to manipulate my body and its chemistry, rather than allow it to do the work that it's programmed to do.

Aside from the fact that I trust her completely, with my entire life, I'm inclined to do it because I don't feel 100% while taking these chemicals, although I'm taking them all exactly as prescribed. I had assumed that medications were designed and prescribed by doctors to help their patients heal. Oh how wrong I was. Despite the fact that I take them religiously, exactly as instructed, I feel overall unwell, off, fearful and anxious.

The fear is persistent. Like me. I refuse to identify myself with my diagnosis because my mind refuses to accept that stroke and young people go together. It hasn't reconciled that event yet. It's unlikely that it ever will. I see the pity in people when they hear about my stroke, and I just can't deal with the idea of sharing, over and over, all the details of everything that happened. There's this huge disconnect that grows bigger by the day. Deep in my mind, I'm done with the stroke. And I mean **done**. But the fear of a second stroke that recurs each time I come into contact with those medications clashes hard with my "I'm done with stroke" mentality.

It pulls me back into the abyss of fear. It's exhausting to keep climbing out of that abyss, because more than anything, I want to move on and focus on healing. The more I try to keep my mind on healing, the more I'm pulled back towards fear each time I see the bottles of pills – they're a constant reminder of "you're at risk of another stroke". I dive deep into researching like I'm paid for it, so I can learn everything I can. I read a lot of stories. People love to share their stories. They're mainly sad. Most are about how the "survivors" are in a wheelchair, or paralyzed on one side of the body. But none of these "survivors" are as young as I am.

I can't come to terms with how I feel physically and mentally and with having to accept feeling like shit just to avoid another stroke. Deep within me, everything is telling me that there is a way to feel 100% **and** prevent a second stroke. I'm so convinced of it, I feel it in the very depth of every cell of my being. I just need to find out how to do it.

As I shift into a new state of awareness, thanks to my journaling and meditation, I become more and more aware of the long-term side effects of the medications. Side-effects like diarrhea, dry mouth, headaches, liver and kidney damage – these are all the price I pay to merely reduce, not eliminate, the risk of a subsequent stroke.

I'm not at all convinced that blood thinners are the holy grail of stroke prevention. They can do damage, and I'm also not willing to trade this for that, so to speak. It's just not the price I'm willing to pay.

Since I have such a severe allergy – as I call it – to following the crowd and obediently doing as I'm told, I'm compelled to seek out the alternatives and the obscure therapies of the ancient healers.

I start with a simple Google search of natural blood thinners or anticoagulants. A whole new world opens up to me with that very search. As I read all the information out there, I become angry at the fact that doctors don't share this information with their patients – that the right food is medicine and that the right foods are healing.

Many articles describe the health benefits of cayenne pepper and turmeric. I learn that turmeric is a natural anti-inflammatory and a very important blood thinner that keeps the blood clean. Usually, blood thickens and clots when it's full of crap. It creates constraints on the inside walls of the veins and in the blood vessels, which in turn prevents blood from flowing properly. I'm on two different medications to take care of that. Well, turmeric and cayenne pepper take care of both of them.

And then it clicks – this is my opportunity to help other people see the light and save them from going through everything I've been going through. And just like that, I transmute the anger into passion, all while going against medical advice once again.

I discover the potential of herbs like cilantro – a powerful detoxifier of heavy metals. *"Oh my God, if people knew how to use all this information, they would be their own doctor!"* I think to myself.

The more I read, the more I understand that I can fully take care of my health all by myself by eating all the powerful roots, herbs, fruits, veggies, nuts and seeds that are available, many of which have medicinal properties. I rediscover my passion for nutrition from a whole new angle. Initially, I loved nutrition for fueling my gym workouts. Now I love it for how it heals. Food can do so so much.

The change is fast. Within a week of ditching the anxiety and diarrhea-inducing chemical medications I feel so much better. I'm not yet ready to tell anyone about this because I would hear how I'm at high risk, blah blah blah. So I gather up all the pills and return them to a few pharmacies, saying I found them while cleaning my medicine cabinet.

I just don't have it in me to flush them down the toilet, because I know by doing so, all these chemicals would end up in the water supply, and ultimately in the water from people's kitchen and bathroom faucets.

Although pharmacies most likely dump medication in a way that it ends up in the water supply anyway, I don't want that on my own conscience.

"I never lose. I either win or learn."

Nelson Mandela

CHAPTER 11
Working Through ♡

The New Normal

I'm fighting. Constantly. For many things. Mainly to get my old life back. That, for me, is the "new normal", or the building of a new life, like I so wished in the hospital. I don't yet understand that there's an error in my thinking, that there's no way back...that my life will never be the same. I'm not the same anymore. The old me is forever gone and so is my old life.

I'm completely oblivious to the fact that I'm being reborn.

I'm so anxious to get back to everything that was my life and my comfort zone that I decide to go back to work. And as has always been the case with me, when I decide something, there's no changing my mind. Returning to work will at least give me a shred of my old life back. I go against Inner Me's pleas again, though she warns me that I should stay home longer and concentrate on building my new life so that it can be sustainable. Ego reminds me of how being back at work would let me see my friends and be around my support network. I couldn't agree more, as most of my co-workers have been through divorce so they'll be there for me as beacons of light on the treacherous path of the looming divorce, all while trying to get myself back to 100% from the effects of the medication crap.

"Those women are my soul sisters, they'll hold my hand and be by my side when I need to talk, to cry or to just vent," I tell myself, in an effort to justify my desire to get back to work so quickly.

I ask my doctor to let me go back to work. I convince her that as a separated woman and a single mom, it's absolutely essential to keep my stress levels down, and having a sense of something that's still stable in my life provides that for me. It's a beautiful sob story, how I've lost everything. "I lost my family when I lost my marriage and I lost my health and my sense of self when I had the stroke. I need to go back to the office because I need something familiar." She agrees to let me go back on modified duties and on a trial basis. However, I want everything. All or nothing. Some parts of us will never change.

For me, the need to go back to work seems obvious now. I'm done with the stroke and any memory of it and I know how to eat and take care of myself. And in true Simone fashion, back to work I go. Fuck the modified hours and fuck the modified duties. I want all of that aspect of my life back! The eight hours at the office, the hour commute each way and the lunches with my girls. The memory of how my job hurts my soul has melted. Like ice cream.

The fact that I work in non-clinical healthcare doesn't help me. At all. I'm constantly surrounded by nurses who have moved into executive and management positions, all vying for the chance to steer healthcare in a good direction. Good by clinical standards, that is. Definitely not by my personal human standards – not by a long shot. Still, I willingly lower my standards just so that I can get a piece of my past back. It's one of those familiar things – a comfort zone where pain doesn't exist and you don't have to worry about being uncomfortable. Familiarity sure is safer and more stable than the upheaval of my current post-stroke, post-separation life.

The first day back at work is nothing like I expect. As soon as I'm back in the office, I'm ambushed by curious, well-meaning colleagues who want step-by-step details of exactly what I felt during the stroke, how long it lasted, where I was when it happened, how I was feeling right before it happened. On and on it goes. Multiple times.

To say that the welcome back is overwhelming is an understatement. Having to tell so many people the details of something I want to forget is exhausting. How do I stop this? There's enough on my plate already: eight-hour work days, the bumper-to-bumper commute, being a single parent to two growing boys and taking care of myself and the household, as any woman would.

Although I understand they care, it still irritates me how everyone thinks I shouldn't be working. Nobody really asks what I need or want. Instead there are a lot of opinions. A lot of "knowledge". Incredible how so many people seem to know what other people want so well. I wonder if they all know what they want for themselves and their lives as much as they seem to know what others want.

I'm 37, and the uncertainty around how I will rebuild my life continues. The questions keep coming, but not the answers. How is my life going to evolve? Am I going to find someone to date? A life partner? Will I get married again? Should I? Should I just stick to dating?

I decide to just live my life to the fullest in the moment and to keep away from fear. I change my eating habits. Completely. I tap into my strong discipline and focus. I stop eating meat and other animal products. I'm vegan, as they call it.

Others ridicule this new lifestyle, but convinced I'm on the right path. I ditch my omelettes and pancakes, order an expensive Vitamix blender and start my mornings with fruit smoothies. And of course, I include nature's medicine – turmeric, cayenne, ginger and herbs. That becomes my daily breakfast.

I join Jowita and stop eating anything cooked. I feel amazing. My mind is sharp and alert. I'm light on my feet and I have a lot of energy. No brain fog, no fatigue. My metabolism is on fire, my digestion is speeding up and I feel physically better than I have in what feels like decades. *"I wish I knew this 10, 15, 20 years ago. I would have stopped eating what I was eating and done all this in a heartbeat, just so that I can feel this good"* I think to myself. For a split second I wonder whether I would've even had a stroke, had I adopted this diet and lifestyle back then. *"And I sure as hell would've never drugged myself with painkillers, antibiotics, blood thinners and any other synthetic chemicals made in a lab, especially since Mother Nature has made everything we need to heal ourselves."*

I start my own little business training women and teaching them how to eat so they can lose weight. The first footprint of my new life.

My routine is comforting and feels safe: pay bills all by myself, spend time with the kids, train my clients. I try very hard to create some consistency and prevent another disruption. And I do. My relationship with Frank is stable, work is good, I have my children with me, my health and my little business are thriving, so life is good. I buy my own property and go back to school.

When life is good, it's **good**. So much so that good just flows to me. Good opportunities, continued good health and good – no, make that amazing – people.

I meet people who will forever be my soul family, like generous Connie, a fellow personal trainer who is so great, she offers me clients and opportunities that lead to an increased income for me. Like amazing, giving Elisabeth, my schoolmate, who opens her home to me and gives me free treatments without ever expecting anything in return.

Good just keeps coming my way. In fact, good happens even in situations I don't expect.

New Milestones

My relationship with Frank is incredibly positive and I am so proud of us. We are really great friends and have each other's backs. He's very patient and helps me anytime I need it. The children thrive. No stress, no worry for them. They are our focus and we're on the same page where they're concerned. Everyone is doing incredibly great and thriving.

In 2015, I can't be any happier. I have officially made it. It's my 40th birthday! Another important birthday to celebrate. Another big party. Frank and all the important people in my life are present to celebrate – not my birthday, but rather to celebrate life. Life is a precious, very fragile and beautiful thing.

Today's party couldn't be any more different from the one four years earlier. I'm different too. My appearance comes second. Now it's more about being healthy, being around for the kids, being an example of health to them so that they can see. And they do see.

Children are great teachers. My boys see me learning, gaining knowledge. And their trust and belief in me are absolutely empowering. My habit of listening to one of my mentor's lectures as I do things around the house is quite infectious. Dr. Morse always emphasizes the importance of repetition. And he repeats things himself, like reminding us that everything is curable, that there is no disease that does not have a cure. So my kids now know that everything is curable. They have no sense of fear like I did. I admire them for that and I'm grateful that I was able to shed light on this fact for them.

In 2016, I graduate from the Cellular Regenerative Detoxification program where I learned all there is to know about natural nutrition and detoxification, having been taught by one of the greatest healers and teachers in natural medicine – Dr. Robert Morse. He is the one who taught me all about how everything can be cured and that there is no disease that does not have a cure. It's the most liberating feeling in the world, bar none. My fear of ever getting sick has completely disappeared, thanks to this amazing doctor. Even my children have no worries about it. They now know that no matter what happens, mom will help them heal.

Sure, people get sick, but they can 100% get well again, if they so desire. Desire is always the first step. Decision is the second.

At this stage the only negative in my life is my office job, which is less and less appealing. Perhaps the stroke has changed me too much and the new me just doesn't belong in this particular work environment. Yet, I'm tightly holding onto a stressful job I can barely tolerate.

Since graduating from my recent studies, I've become obsessed with telling people how easy it is to support your body so it can heal. I'm continually doing this for myself – investing in my health.

I'm so used to having this job and it pays the bills. Perhaps subconsciously I am too scared to leave the last piece of my pre-stroke life behind. Perhaps because it feels safe. Familiar.

Yet everything else is new in my life, so this job just doesn't fit anymore.

October is a special month. Not just because I was born this month and most of my closest friends are October babies too, but because life-changing events typically take place in October for me.

The stroke was in 2011. Then, in October 2018, mere days after my birthday, my tenure as an employee comes to a complete end. I move all my energy and all my focus to self-employment and to running my own business.

The universe made it so that I have the time to shape my future exactly the way I want to and build my business like I built my health. Like I built my new life. I can write books and help more people. Though there's a lot of uncertainty, the unknown sparks a sense of excitement in me, because I understand how the greatest control is the control over myself, not over my surroundings.

I have the control of making my life exactly what I want it to be and I love the idea that it's not going towards another job.

For me, the opportunity to run my business is confirmation from the universe that now I'm ready. That I should stop holding on to things while I'm trying to move on. If you're trying to move forward into the future, you can't have one foot stuck firmly in the past.

I'm deeply grateful that I got my lesson about life and living from my stroke. Truly, wholeheartedly living, being fierce instead of living in fear.

"Always fall asleep thinking of what you want to achieve, never about things that happened in the past. Leave the past in the past," a mentor once said to me. I look forward to that nightly ritual.

"Here we are. What else do you want to achieve, Madam CEO?" asks Ego. Madam CEO. Well, I am running my own show after all.

"You don't know the list of my future achievements?" I ask Ego, with an audible laugh.

"Tell me again," he says, excited.

The list of my future achievements

1.   Live 100% on my terms

2.   Write books

3.   Self-mastery

4. Help others (never have to go through what I went through)

5. Go to Hawaii

6. Launch another business

7. Buy a convertible Porsche

8. Move to Florida

9. Learn other healing modalities like hypnosis

10. Eliminate limiting beliefs

11. Become a multi-millionaire

12. Buy more property

13. Get married

"Well, first, I want to write a book about all this. Then go to Hawaii, then study Hypnosis, move to sunny Florida...."

Thoughts and visuals of my list of achievements – really, they are dreams come true – float in my mind as I close my eyes and enter a peaceful sleep.

"I think the things you most regret in life are things you didn't do."

Steve Jobs

CHAPTER 12
Turning Inside ♡

Madam CEO

"Okay guys, roll your sleeves and let's get started on that list," I announce to Ego and Inner Me full of excitement as soon as I wake up. That list is still lingering in my mind when I open my eyes. There's something about new beginnings that excites me in ways I can't describe with words. Inner Me and Ego don't need words. They know. They are part of the fabric of my being so they understand my feelings and my emotions. They know this excitement very well. They've been with me through all my ups and downs after all. Excitement and new beginnings have been part of my journey thus far.

"Alright Madam CEO, I'm ready to hit the ground running. What's on the agenda?" asks Ego, full of energy. *"May I suggest we start with that convertible Porsche?"* he adds full of mischief. He's clearly thinking of adventure here. *"I'm actually surprised you didn't aim higher, like Ferrari....Lamborghini,"* he adds.

I let out an audible laugh.

"I love the way you think," I respond with a huge smile.

I do love Italian cars and I would most definitely love a badass sports luxury car like a Ferrari or Lamborghini. It would quench my thirst for speed. I've dreamed of driving Italian sport luxury since I got the taste of it in Switzerland a few years prior while driving my friend's Ferrari Spider in the Swiss Alps.

Inner Me is silent. Listening to me and Ego, and assessing.

"Maybe we should work on the millions first since they are necessary for such extravagances," I add.

"Ooook," he responds, in an acquiescing tone. *"Let's settle for the Porsche."*

"Settle?" I ask and let out a laugh again. *"Let me remind you that I already settled when I bought the 328 instead of the 135,"* I say, referring to the last BMW I bought. It would not be the last.

I really wanted a 2-door, but I "settled" for the 4-door since I transport the boys and sometimes mom and dad; so this "settling" was solely for the comfort of my passengers. But in reality, it's not **really** settling because I love German cars. German is all I've driven since I got my license. I'm a bit like a kid in a candy store so to speak when it comes to cars - I want to drive them all. Luckily, I've learned how to pace myself; but I certainly am familiar with everything the candy store offers.

"I've always wanted a Porsche. This is precisely why it's on my list of future achievements. Settle..." I say out loud, trailing off. I roll my eyes and shake my head in disbelief that Ego would consider such a luxury sports car settling.

As I was ready to move on with my thoughts, Inner Me makes her entrance into the conversation. *"Simone, you already have a car that's perfect. It runs well, it's reliable and it does the job."*

"You're right," I respond.

After all her pleas that Saturday back in 2011 when lightning struck inside my head, I have learned that she is **never** wrong and that everything she says, she says for my well-being and 100% for my benefit. I don't ignore her anymore and I always do what she suggests.

They don't say "Listen to your gut" or "What does your gut say?" for no good reason.

She is my trusted "gut".

"So, what do you suggest we start on, from that list?" I ask her.

"What would you like to tackle first?" she answers my question with a question of her own.

This is my usual response when I want to hear what the other person has to say on the topic at hand. She has taught me this tactic very well.

"I defer to you," I respond, keen on finding out what she would advise.

"Self-mastery," she answers instantly.

"WHAT??? Ugh, of course she wouldn't suggest something fun," laments Ego. *"What's wrong with the Porsche?"* he challenges Inner Me.

I jump in. *"Hold on a second. She's right. You know this."*

"How?" he asks. *"What exactly is wrong with the Porsche? You already have a car. It's not like I'm suggesting you buy a plane,"* he says in exasperation. *"You're just exchanging your present car, for another one, that's all,"* he adds, convinced that the purchase would be 100% justified. *"And may I add that you'd be exchanging a German car for another German car."*

Inner Me ignores him completely.

*"Do you want to **buy** things or do you want to **invest** in things?"* she asks me, knowing that I understand the difference.

A purchase is money spent on something that gives very little to no return. An investment is money spent on something that gives a significant return.

"If you buy the Porsche, you'll buy a liability," she adds. *"Think of the maintenance costs. And insurance."*

I know that a car depreciates significantly even after you drive it off the lot. Then there are the other costs associated with owning a luxury car.

"I want to invest," I respond instantly.

I didn't even have to think about it because I felt the rightness of that answer. I don't know how she does it, but she always lets me feel the right or the wrong of my answers and decisions physically. That's how she guides me. It's her gift.

"What do you want to invest in?" she continues.

"Myself." No hesitation there.

"Excellent. This will lead you to all those other things on your list," she adds calmly.

"Great. Keep listening to her and say goodbye to ever having any fun," says Ego, in an offended, no filter tone.

We both ignore him.

Priorities

Truth is, though I read Louise Hay's book and turned to affirmations, meditation and journaling, most of my healing journey was very focused on healing my brain and keeping my body healthy. I studied nutrition and cellular detoxification because I wanted to learn how to heal anything that afflicts the body.

I wanted to know how to help others do the same, the natural way. I wanted to know how to get rid of things that everyone always complained about, especially since most of these "diseases" were caused by lifestyle. So easy to reverse. My mentor, Dr. Morse was helping people reverse these things every day, and I wanted to learn how to do the same. Health is a vast topic and there was never any lack of things to learn when it comes to it. New research was being done on a regular basis, new protocols were being tried out, and new ideas were being brought to light. Learning about health could never end.

I was still putting all my focus outward, on the outer world, and limiting the self-exploration work to reading, affirmations, journaling and meditation. While I yearned to get to know the new me, somehow, I had remained stuck in the never-ending pursuit of information about health. Dad's cancer helped fuel that pursuit, and the vast amount of information that's available online lured me into spending endless hours researching, that very little time would be left for maintaining my household, never mind self-exploration.

There was that growing desire inside me to get to know myself on a deeper level because everything outside me showed that I **was** a new person. I was no longer an employee, nor the married, gym obsessed, motorcycle riding chick anymore. I was now a divorced woman, single mom, holistic health school graduate, business owner, sedan driver and hospital escapee – not necessarily in that order.

Those were all my external world transformations, but what transformed internally? How had I grown and evolved emotionally? Mentally? Spiritually? I had clearly grown and evolved since the gym obsession had disappeared and I had no desire to ride anymore. I had even outgrown some people. Going out no longer involved loud crowded places where people gathered mainly to drink; now dinner in a quiet restaurant or get togethers at friends' houses where we would cook together and exchange life stories was bliss.

Deep down I knew I needed solitude and no distractions to be able to scratch the surface of getting to know the new Simone, but living in a busy city, being a mom, running a business and studying made solitude nearly impossible. And they were all a good excuse to postpone that work for the "more calm times". It was daunting enough to keep up with the daily requirements of a healthy life, and for being successful – go to bed early, wake up early, do yoga, floss your teeth, write down your goals, read 10 pages a day, meditate, journal, be present with the kids, spend time with friends, be a good daughter, keep in touch with clients, post on social media, eat homemade meals, slow down, go for a walk, declutter, etc. etc. etc.; to add self-exploration to that already long list was asking for anxiety.

I looked into finding a remote place and doing a silent retreat. God knows I needed it. Looking back at the years that had passed between my marriage to Frank starting to fall apart and the day I was finally free from my government job, all I see is a treacherous road full of fear and pain, peppered with some great achievements.

What stood out was the pain. Fear I had conquered for the most part, but the pain was still there, safely tucked away in the deep corners of my mind and my soul. The feelings of pain from the separation were left untouched since the stroke arrived and remained untouched while I concentrated on healing. The stroke came into my life with such force, I had no choice but to deal with it, to the exclusion of all else. I **had to** get better so I can function at least for the kids.

I needed to come face to face with the pain and see where it came from. This time, not for the kids but for me.

I had wondered about when Inner Me would nudge me about it in a way that made it impossible to ignore.

Self-work of this kind was foreign to me. I had never done it and it's not like they teach it in school. You learn it yourself. Organically. Often, while being just with yourself. Looking back on my life, I lived at home until I moved in with Frank, dating was something I did in my very early 20s, and earning a living involved having a job and being an employee, not running my own business.

My new life, living on my own, paying the bills alone, dating, and running my own business required a different person, a different Simone. Living on my own I had gotten accustomed to, but dating was a whole new world. Like going from a park straight to the jungle. The rules of dating had changed drastically over the 20 years that had passed. I was entering that world as a full-grown woman with a divorce **and** a critical illness under my belt. I had not taken a course to familiarize myself with the rules of dating in your 40s or learn how to navigate the treacherous jungle. Meeting people was incredibly difficult. Dating them, even more so.

As for running a business, I had to unlearn everything I had learned as a government employee and eliminate habits I had developed working as one for 15 years. That's the thing about being an employee, it can be really great. Even I embraced it once upon a time. It didn't really involve that much work. Everything was set up. It just required you to show up and do. I loved walking into the office and having everything there. I never had to chase or create work. It was always patiently waiting there for me every day, in abundance. Teams of people took care of everything. Receptionists answered the phones, IT teams maintained the computers and the systems, marketing teams took care of all the marketing material and the executives took care of the big decisions. It was so perfect. A well-oiled machine. As a business owner, you have to develop the systems, create the work, find the clients, serve them and stay on top of your craft. Entrepreneurship is definitely not for the faint of heart.

Here I was doing it all, and all on my own. Sometimes I was surprised - did I do all this within 24 hours a day?

"I don't even know that I have the time for this self-exploration work," I confess to Inner Me and Ego as I get in bed and turn off the light one night. *"I know how important it is, but seriously, when would I make time for that too?"*

"Are you sure?" asks Inner Me calmly.

"About what?"

"Not having the time."

"You know I am super busy."

"Let's talk about this Simone," she says gently.

"Oh oh, here we go," says Ego. *"She's going to try to convince you that you **need** to do this. Like you'll die without it. You two need to chill. I still say you need that Porsche and let loose for a while. All you do is work, study and other boring shit,"* h*e* adds rolling his eyes.

Hmm. I see what he means and by most standards, it does qualify as boring, but I actually enjoy doing all that. I could very easily become a professional student. I **love** learning.

"All you do is listen to lectures and podcasts. When was the last time you watched a comedy? Listened to a song and danced?" he continues with his complaints.

"He's got a point," I say out loud.

"You never do anything fun, and you don't laugh."

"That's not true," I shoot back. *"I laugh with Roman all the time."*

Roman and I got into the habit of tickling each other. We wait for the most opportune time, and when the other is least expecting it we deliver a jab in the ribs with one finger. We then continue with a barrage of more jabs in the neck area and on the other side of the ribs. He calls it "tasering". I initiated it. Roman would get into the fetal position on the bed or on the couch, depending on where I would catch him, and laugh uncontrollably as I continue to tickle him, wrapping himself in the blanket to keep me at bay, sometimes calling out for Marcus or whoever was around to help him.

He turned that around on me many times, and would send **me** in the fetal position trying to keep him at bay. Priceless moments of sheer fun and joy, even though Roman is now a teenager and not the 5-year-old little boy anymore.

"Fair enough, but you definitely don't do enough of that," he responds. I couldn't agree more.

"I guess you're right. I definitely need a break from the monotony of studying and working and such."

While Ego is full of excitement and Inner Me intrigued about my suggestions, I pause and an idea comes to me......a nice vacation. With my boys.

"Yes, yes yes!!" I make Ego very happy.

"What a great idea," adds Inner Me. There would be time for self-mastery work during this trip, as I'm not taking the laptop, and I should have all the time in the world for myself. The idea of self-work is more and more appealing. I'm really planning to do this. Inner Me comes in helping.

"If you commit a few minutes to self-discovery every day, you will make such incredible progress in continuing your growth," says Inner Me. *"Keep asking yourself important questions and focus on finding the answers."*

Ego jumps back in. *"You say this like without doing all kinds of work, she will perish."*

"No one is catastrophizing anything here. Stop," I say to him, rolling my eyes. These two are really on a roll now. Have they forgotten it's me they are talking about?

"No such thing could ever happen. Growth and evolution are inevitable, and happen by default, but it's most fulfilling when you are an active participant in it all, rather than sitting back and letting it happen to you. As an active participant, you are in essence the captain and you steer the ship in the direction you wish it to go; otherwise it goes in whatever direction the wind takes it; that way it may get beached or it can crash," she explains calmly.

"I see," says Ego, processing the information.

"Well, I always steered the ship," I say. *"All my doom and gloom thoughts steered the ship to a crash. We can all agree that the stroke was quite the spectacular crash, right?"* I add with a laugh.

I can laugh about the stroke now. It's been years and I've been feeling amazing. My diet is on point and really dialed in. I haven't taken a pill since the anticoagulants and other crap I had been put on immediately post-stroke. My body now functions like a well-oiled machine.

"Oh, it sure was," replies Ego.

"I'm glad you recognize that Simone. Thoughts really do become things," says Inner Me. *"Your growth is definitely underway and you have made such great progress. You should be proud of yourself just for recognizing that thing alone. We are both so proud of you,"* she adds lovingly.

"We definitely are, however, I still say you need to have more fun baby," says Ego, encouragement and love in his tone.

"But remember, self-mastery requires you to conquer the pain too, as you did fear," adds Inner Me, completely disregarding Ego's remark about fun.

A knot in my throat and that familiar feeling in the pit of my stomach appear immediately after her comment.

Truth is, the pain of the separation and divorce remained stuffed down all this time while I concentrated on the constant work I did related to healing my brain, getting off the meds, going to school and launching my own business. All that kept me really busy. And really distracted from the most important work I needed to do.

"Anyways, guys I'm going on vacation," I announce, ignoring both of their comments.

I jump out of bed, turn on the light and open my laptop. I call the boys who are at Frank's and present the idea to them. In 30 minutes, I have the tickets booked. 11 weeks later we are on the beach, soaking up the sun.

I give Ego all the fun he wants on this vacation. We frolic in the water, play games, meet people, interact with the locals, stay up late, listen to music, dance....we let loose.

Travelling is so much more than just going on vacation. It lets you take a break from the stresses and monotony of daily life and work. You meet the locals and see how they live. It makes you appreciate all you have. You see a new world, you meet new people, you make new connections, you are removed from the distractions of your everyday life and work, so you come back refreshed and with a different perspective. A vacation renews you.

I make the boys and giving them a great time my priority. No thought given to self-mastery. My guilt of having been away from them during the stroke justifies me concentrating on them, so I push self-work aside. And besides, they are my responsibility, so I have to keep them safe.

Self-mastery and coming face to face with my pain has to wait a bit longer.

"When people are determined, they can overcome anything."

Nelson Mandela

CHAPTER 13

Conquering the Pain

The Work

The get-away is just a distraction and I know it. A good distraction. Putting my kids first, and not myself. At this point, I see my limitations I had set for myself, and now I have the urge to break through.

Inner Me's words about conquering the pain echo through my mind every single day. They are like a gentle tap on the shoulder to say *"Please don't forget to address your pain"* or *"You really need to address that pain Simone"*.

Deep inside I know that I need to work through all that, but truthfully, I don't want to come face to face with it. Not just yet.

Was I afraid? Scared? Fearful? Of doing some soul searching? ME?? SCARED???

"Nah," says Ego intruding.

"You made fear bow down to you already; fear is your bitch. You've been there and killed that," he adds with a laugh.

There is the reason why I always loved Ego, he always knows how to empower me.

"So what do you think it is?" I ask him.

"Don't look to me to do your work, sweetheart," he retorts. *"Look inside and find your answers."*

"Ha," exclaims Inner Me. *"Look who's running from doing work,"* she adds, pointing right at Ego.

"Well, she needs to jog her memory and find what thoughts led her down the path of pain, not me," he snaps back. *"It wasn't me that gave attention to those thoughts; it was her."*

"Okay guys, I get it. Stop bickering," I say exasperated. *"I need to do the work. I'll do it."*

I know that I can't run away from this anymore. The thoughts, the feelings, the emotions....everything about the pain is safely locked inside of me, so no matter where I go, it is there, with me. But in the end, even though the pain is locked inside me, I am its prisoner, not the other way around.

Another dragon to slay.....another demon to conquer.

My chats with Inner Me immediately post-stroke were the most enriching transformative conversations that really helped me progress my healing. So, it only reasons that she should be my #1 go to for all my advice in this work too. And here was my opportunity to address something proactively, rather than run the risk of it becoming something bigger that will take over my life. The opportunity to steer my ship and avoid another crash.

On impulse I book a yoga retreat trip to the Bahamas. I need time without distractions so that I can put a dent in the self-work.

The Release

I intentionally didn't bring any books to read, no laptop, just my phone so I can take pictures. I wanted nothing to distract me. I chose this retreat at the advice of a friend because it involved doing yoga, meditation and chanting. In the Bahamas. I had never been to the Bahamas but heard that it was absolutely gorgeous. I love the Caribbean and the islands.

Though I knew I'd be surrounded by others, including my friend whom I was sharing my room with, I planned to have some me time so I could start the work, with Ego and Inner Me in my corner for support.

A little dingy boat took me, my friend and a few fellow seekers of inner peace to the ashram on Paradise Island, which just so happened to be located literally right next to the famous Atlantis resort.

Fellow seekers of inner peace, as well as yogis that had come from all corners of the world to learn how to teach the ancient Indian discipline, were the kindest, most loving, most humble and most welcoming people I had ever met. Some were practicing silence.

I too wanted to adopt silence and communicate strictly with Inner Me and Ego until the pain inside me dissipated. An ambitious goal for the short week I would be here. I decided that I would forego the silence for now and concentrate on yoga and working through the pain.

I knew this was the right place to do this work; the island itself is gorgeous, the weather heavenly, the beach pristine and inviting, with turquoise water, white, fine sand and beautiful palm trees. There's also yoga, meditation and chanting for deep spiritual practice. And if you want some excitement and fun, there's always the lively Atlantis right next door. It's beyond perfect.

The ashram has very strict rules. Yoga classes are available throughout the day, two simple vegetarian meals are included and meditation plus chanting takes place daily. The pleasant ring of the bell is heard every morning well before the sun rises, inviting all guests to come chant and prepare the mind for meditation. Meditation would typically follow, with guests coming in throngs to achieve the ultimate state of relaxation and a tranquil, still mind, devoid of rushing thoughts. The perfect way to start the day.

I settle into a routine quickly because I want to get as much as I could out of this experience and get the ball rolling on self-work and conquering the pain.

Every morning I run the beach and walk it with my friend and other ladies again at sunset. It's during these runs that I am able to empty my mind since I am forced to shift my focus on the feelings of the body – my aching muscles, my lungs, on fire and feeling like they're about to burst open, and my heart that's beating so fast that it's about to jump out of my chest.

Self-mastery work underway.

On day four, in the morning, after my run, with the sun peeking over the horizon and nothing but the sound of the waves to distract me, I sit alone on the sand facing the ocean and call on Inner Me and Ego to start the journey inwards to face the pain.

"How long do you guys think it will take me to resolve the pain? To get rid of it?" I ask full of trepidation.

"The only way out is to go through it" responds Inner Me. *"There is no set time and no shortcut if you are looking for one."*

I sigh audibly.

"Can we do this another time? Maybe when I get back home?" I ask, trying to get out of the work.

"I thought this is what you came here to do," says Ego. *"Scared?"* he challenges me.

"Actually yes, a little," I respond.

"Of what?" he continues. *"This is familiar territory. You're not dealing with something new here baby. You got this,"* he encourages me. *"And we're both here,"* he continues referring to himself and Inner Me.

"You can do this Simone," says Inner Me, reinforcing Ego's encouragement. *"But most importantly, you **need** to do this."*

"Okay fine, let's do it," I say, my heart skipping a beat.

"Let the thoughts come up, watch them and let them float away, do not engage them, do not call them back, do not hang on to them. Let them go," Inner Me instructs.

I fold my legs in lotus position and close my eyes.

"Okay, let's see it. All of it," I say out loud.

My mind goes to Frank, to mom, to dad, to friends who I thought had been true friends, to exes, to coworkers, to strangers, to teachers, to family members, to bosses, to acquaintances, to classmates.

A tidal wave of thoughts from years passed come rushing, hitting my empty mind with brute force, each thought vying for my attention. Hateful words said by others, disappointing words, broken promises, lies, and words of deception and betrayal echo in the chambers of my mind.

Fat tears spill out of my eyes. My heart rate increases, my muscles tighten and my breath shortens.

"Breathe," commands Inner Me quietly.

I start to sob, unable to catch my breath as the thoughts continue to thrust their poison dipped daggers into my mind. I let the pain of all those memories wash over me.

"Breathe," commands Inner Me again.

I sob remembering the fights, the confrontations, the discussions, the injustices, the abandonment, the accusations, the rage, the anger, the horrible interactions. Years of memories of sadness, sorrow, loss and grief play vividly on the screen of my mind.

"Breathe," Inner Me reminds me.

Then comes all my bullshit - all my sins, all my lies, all my insecurities, all my failures, all my jealousy, all my judgment, all my selfishness, and all my pride.

I see it all, I hear it all, I feel it all, I remember it all. I hang my head in shame at the reality that I was no saint. I complained all about these people and how they wronged me, but here I was face to face with my own darkness. It stung. It hurt.

"Stay with it Simone," says Inner Me. *"I know it's not easy, but you are healing."*

"And you are amazing," adds Ego. *"And so strong."*

It's the furthest thing from easy. I feel every shred of anger and disappointment, sorrow, guilt, shame and sadness, as if for the first time again. Years of it all keep crashing into my mind, my heart and soul like ocean waves that keep crashing against the shore on a windy day. Relentlessly.

"You must forgive them," says Inner Me. *"All of them. And yourself."*

"It's the only way to let it all go. And you know that most of them didn't intend to hurt you. They didn't plan it or strategize it. They just didn't know any better," she adds.

"Take the time to tell each person that you forgive them and send them love. Say it out loud," she guides me. *"Imagine all the pain that each person inflicted on you as a balloon and release the balloon, one by one. One balloon, one person. Some balloons are bigger than others."*

Tears still flowing, I go through the list of people who stand out in my mind and tell each one *"I forgive you and send you love."* Then I imagine the pain from each one morphing into a red balloon which I release and watch float away to join the white fluffy clouds littering the sky above.

"You must also forgive yourself. It's imperative. And say the same to yourself. Then release the balloon," says Inner Me.

I stay there for what feels like hours, as every thought and every emotion flows through my very being before I release it to the sky above.

And then it ends. The emotional and spiritual surgery to remove a big tumor of toxic thoughts and emotions is done. With no anaesthetic. I felt every shred of pain all over again. Nothing is left inside but a vast, clean, luminous space. My body relaxes and my breathing slows down. A huge weight has just been lifted off my soul. I am exhausted.

I stretch out my legs and lay back on the sand. I open my eyes and look at the blue sky above, imagining red balloons as tiny little dots floating higher and higher.

"Wow baby, I bow down to you," exclaimed Ego. *"You did it."*

"It starts with you and ends with you," says Inner Me. *"You did something really extraordinary."*

The remainder of my time in the Bahamas is spent doing yoga on the beach, meditating, chanting and doing the walks with the ladies at night.

The simplicity of it all feels so right and so amazing. Just nature, yoga and meditation. I could really get used to this life. But I do miss the boys. A lot.

"Whatever you are thinking about, you will attract."

Bob Proctor

CHAPTER 14

Studying Me

The Hunger

I hit the ground running, renewed, refreshed and lighter when I get back home. The grudges had weighed a lot. I sign up for more courses, hungry for more knowledge, eager to learn and be able to offer my clients more.

In my mind, I go back to the Bahamas trip again and again. Even when I'm taking my baths by candlelight. I know I want to go back to the ashram. It had really been a life-changing experience.

I rest my head against the wall behind me and close my eyes, momentarily transported back to that transformative morning on the beach.

Forgiveness is so powerful. All this time, I had been held hostage by those thoughts and those feelings, imprisoned by my own unwillingness to resolve it all and let it go. *"Why didn't you guys hound me to get that work done sooner?"* I ask slowly. *"You know I want to get to the root of all my bullshit. What is it that's had me trapped in it all these years?"*

I decided that I would continue the work, because I really wanted to find out what exactly it was that caused me so much pain and kept me stuck in thought patterns that didn't serve me. I needed to rewire my mind and my thought patterns.

The Bahamian beach experience is still fresh in my mind even to this day, so, every once in a while I momentarily think about all the people that hurt me along the years of my life and how I released the pain, balloon by balloon. Otherwise I am in a great place, free from the toxicity of the negative thoughts and grudges I held against them. I am working with my clients, studying and regularly traveling to see Jowita who has now moved to sunny Florida.

Travel has become somewhat of an addiction for me. A short year after my trip to the Bahamas I ask the boys to go to Hawaii – a place I had always dreamed of visiting. It doesn't take much to convince Roman who, like me, and like Ego, is always up for an adventure. Marcus on the other hand, my uber-intellectual first-born, who graduated with honors and has always had stellar grades, turns me down in favor of concentrating on his university studies.

I build a kick-ass itinerary, sparing no expense, fully intending to make this an enriching trip for me and Roman. It is that and so much more. For two glorious weeks, we island hop, swim with stingrays at night, parasail, drive through the mountains, discover black sand beaches and stunning waterfalls, dine in really expensive restaurants, and come face to face with the breathtaking beauty of Hawaii, the likes of which no other part of the world can offer.

Inner Me and Ego are patient and supportive of all my adventures there and provide guidance when I need it.

Ego is instrumental during the Road to Hana trip in Maui when Roman and I drive on the side of a mountain with no barrier for protection. A small mistake could send us to our death in the rocky ocean below. He reminds me of how great of a driver I am and how deeply grateful he is for the exhilarating adventure. He still loves adventure and risk, as do I. Some fundamental parts of me remain unchanged.

Inner Me is full of love and appreciation for this enriching trip and never interferes or warns me of any danger. Not even once. I am clearly doing great. I know I have already made a pretty significant transformation.

I swear, since that cathartic work in the Bahamas, my life and my relationship with these two has gotten so much better; if that was even possible. Their love and support had always been different, depending on their respective characters but always unconditional and fully available to me, no matter what I did and/or said, but something had shifted and things were just so much better somehow. Deeper. Richer. And we were.....closer.

"Imagine how much better it will get once you get the rest of the work done," says Inner Me sweetly one morning in Maui as I was taking in the gorgeous sunrise on the balcony of the condo Roman and I were staying in. And I have no doubt it will. Since the experience and transformation in the Bahamas, I've become quite obsessed with the idea of continuing with the transformation.

What's Ahead?

The rest of the self-work is spontaneous. And quite timely. It's October and the world is still in the middle of chaos that started in the spring. Jowita is getting married. It makes my heart swell to see her this blissfully happy. Fall is all about change – the change of time...the change of seasons...and the change of life. Jowita's journey as a married woman begins. Big change. And October, as it has always done, brings significant life changes my way too.

Another chapter of my transformation happens in Florida. In a castle. In true Jowita fashion, generous as always, she lets me stay alone in the palatial room we shared the night before the wedding; she joins her husband in their suite as newlyweds.

Exhausted from the momentous and eventful day that started very early, I shower and lay in the massive bed. I look out the window at the vast ocean at the foot of the luxurious hotel, and interlace my hands behind my head.

"Fuck, how amazing is this?" I say out loud to Inner Me and Ego.

Sleep is nowhere on the radar, despite how exhausted I am from the busy day that was.

"You mean being here?" asks Ego.

"That too. All of it. Today was incredible," I say, out loud again, with a huge grin on my face.

The day had been incredibly busy. And fulfilling. Every minute had been accounted for. Breakfast, hair, makeup, pre-wedding pictures, steaming the dress, getting dressed for the actual wedding, the wedding itself, more pictures, reception and carrying everything down to the room. I was with Jowita right up to the moment she walked down the aisle, and then sat with her at the head table, basking in the energy of love, happiness and joy.

"Amazing really. And she pulled it all off with such elegance in the middle of this craziness," I add, referring to the world-wide situation at hand.

"You loved it didn't you?" asks Ego.

"I more than loved it," I answer. *"Think about it. Not only did Jowi get married, but I am in Florida, in a luxury hotel. Guys, life fucking rocks,"* I answer sitting up.

I walk over to the massive windows and part the curtains open in one move.

"Look at this," I say loudly and motion to the ocean view. *"I manifested this incredibleness."*

"Yes you did baby, yes you did. Well done. Really well done," exclaims Ego.

"You created this for yourself Simone," says Inner Me. *"You're definitely doing something right."*

"I guess," I say, walking back to the bed and getting under the covers. *"To be honest I don't even know how and what."*

"All through your thoughts and your attention," she tells me.

*"I guess you're right. I **had** been thinking about this and looking forward to it for so long,"* I say, referring to Jowita's wedding.

I was honored to be Jowita's right hand person on her most important day, and I was also getting a vacation out of it. I flew out on my birthday. Not only was I going to see my best friend get married, I was also going to be participating in it **and** be in beautiful Florida **on my birthday**. It couldn't get any better than that.

"Right. It happened so effortlessly, didn't it?" asks Inner Me.

"Yes, it did," I reply.

"Good, positive thoughts about something, plus being so happy about it brought you all that incredibleness as you call it," she tells me. *"And you know, your thoughts don't necessarily have to be the best thoughts, they just have to be thoughts of satisfaction, and contentment, happiness, joy; positive things like that"* she continues.

"So you mean, I have to just have thoughts of satisfaction and happiness, and incredibleness will just flow to me?" I ask, skeptical.

"Yes, and any thoughts that are not positive and satisfying, leave them, don't look at them, don't give them attention," she replies.

"Oh, and don't try to go all 'fake it 'til you make it'. You can't pretend. You know you can't fake satisfaction, happiness and joy," she adds.

"Speaking of 'fake it 'til you make it', people thought I was all good, remember?" I ask, referring to the time when I was lying to the whole world about how I was feeling. *"Everyone bought it."*

"But were you really good back then? Happy? At peace? Satisfied?" she challenges me.

"No, of course not. I was a wreck."

"Ultimately, why did you even care so much about what people thought that you had to go out of your way to put on a show? Did you actually care about whether they thought you were happy or not? asks Ego, eager to jump into the conversation.

*"Did it matter more to you that they **thought** you were happy and okay, or that you actually were happy and okay?"* he continues, full of wisdom.

Those words hit home. He's right. I cared more about what people thought about my level of happiness and whether I was okay than I did about whether I actually felt happy and okay. I cared so much that I was lying to everyone to make them believe things that were not true – but I wasn't happy at all. I was a mess and I was scared.

"Well...." I say.

"Sweetheart, you can't lie to us, we see it all, we feel it all. That 'fake it 'til you make it' bullshit doesn't work on us," he cuts me off, not giving me a chance to answer.

"It's true Simone, you can't lie to yourself," says Inner Me.

She's right too. Lying to myself would also mean lying to them. They are part of me after all.

*"You're so right. I was such an idiot to care so much about what other people thought. So, what do I do when I **don't** have these thoughts of satisfaction and happiness that you speak of? What if I have negative thoughts? I get those all the time, you know?"* I ask.

"Oh we know," Ego responds. *"We know it all. We even know when you get upset, yell and curse at those who cut you off when you drive."*

"Well seriously, they deserve it. Sometimes I wonder how it's even possible that people who are so incapable of driving deserve their license just like us good drivers do. It's unfair that they are even allowed to drive," I say defensively.

Inner Me takes over the conversation again completely ignoring my rant. *"The secret is, when you see an ugly thought come up, about other drivers, friends, family, anyone or anything really, just refocus. Look elsewhere, otherwise as you know that ugly thought will bring its friends with it, and before you know it, there will be a pack of them".*

I remember clearly how the thoughts came in packs when I was hospitalized.

"And they are hard to keep at bay because they are strong in numbers. It's easier to refocus from one single thought than to deal with a barrage of bad thoughts. All thoughts travel in packs, the good and the bad. Take the opportunity

SIMONE L. GISONDI, CHNC

to shift your attention right away, when it's just one bad or one negative thought," she adds.

I feel the rightness of her words. They are nothing new. They tell the same story as all the spiritual giants tell in all their books – Rhonda Byrne, Bob Proctor, Wayne Dyer, Esther Hicks, Tony Robbins......

Proof that we know a lot more than we think we know. Inner Me is reinforcing their advice and their lessons. I'm sure those people's advice came from their own Inner Me's.

"You are not your mistakes. They are what you did, not who you are."

Lisa Lieberman-Wang

CHAPTER 15
Living Fully ♡

Warfare

Negative thoughts.....they always feel like they creep up on my mind. They are not exclusively about other people. They are also about me. In fact, they are usually about me.

I had waged warfare on myself throughout my entire life.

Though fundamentally I want happiness, as everyone does, I don't ever believe that I can have it, nor that I'm deserving of it. My thoughts have reinforced those two ideas my whole life.

"I love you, but I hate you," is the message I constantly send myself. "I love you Simone for all the hard work you have done, for all that you have achieved. You are great. You are amazing. You are strong. You are beautiful."

"Wait, no. I hate my teeth....I hate my nose....I should make more money....I wish I had a better car....a better place, in a better neighbourhood......more friends.....more likes on Facebook.....and on and on it went.

Warfare.

Inner Me's words echo in my mind.

"I don't know why and how so many of my thoughts are always so negative. I don't want them to be," I tell her.

"They are always so negative because you are always practicing them. Each day. Over and over."

She's right. I do that and I do it really well. Practice makes perfect, as they say.

"And they are in direct opposition to who you really are at your core," she says, gentleness pouring out of her words. *"You as a person are good and always inclined for good, so your work is not to try to be good, or to eliminate the bad, for that matter, but rather to focus on all that is good in you and in your life; this will attract all that is good to you."*

I sit silently, processing her words. She is talking about the Law of Attraction. I had read about this in Rhonda Byrne's books.

Ego is silent.

"You don't ever have to retaliate, you don't have to teach everyone a lesson, to let them feel pain like they inflicted on you. And you definitely don't have to point out what you see as your flaws," she continues.

She knows that I had done that in my life. Guilt embraces me and I feel shame hearing those words from her. That truth is hard to swallow. A knot forms in my throat.

"So how do I stop these negative thoughts? How do I keep them away?" I whisper, as tears rush to my eyes.

"Well, if you can train yourself to look at whether thoughts – any thoughts that come – are positive and pleasing to you, and whether they serve you well, you are well on your

way to eliminating everything you deem bad in your life."
Inner Me is full of love, as she has always been. And that
love is always present in her words. No matter how much
they hurt or sting, her words are infused with pure love.

*"When a thought arises about you doing something, ask
yourself 'Is the idea of doing this filling me with happiness
and satisfaction?' So, for example when a driver cuts you
off, and your first impulse is to yell at him, ask yourself 'Is
it satisfying for me to yell at him, call him a name and
curse him?"* she asks.

"Actually yes, yes it is," I respond. I cannot lie to her. I have
always felt satisfied yelling at other drivers even though they
couldn't hear me. I would yell at them alone in my car,
reabsorbing all the negativity of my words floating around.

*"So you feel good after you called someone a name? After
you yelled at them?"* she continues with the questions,
gentle as always. *"Do you feel happy? Uplifted? Does doing
that put you in a state of joy?"*

*"If your answer is yes, keep doing it all, if your answer is
no, then don't do it anymore,"* she adds, not giving me a
chance to answer.

I take her words in. She is so right. Losing it, yelling,
screaming and swearing at other drivers never achieved
more than me feeling really shitty. Physically and mentally.
And what's worse, I would continue driving and dwelling on
it. More thoughts would come. A barrage of them, exactly as
she said. *"What an asshole!"* ... *"I'm in a rush too!"* ..."Who
do you think you are, asshole?"..."How could he do
that?"*...and on and on.

*"And what happens physiologically when you allow
thoughts to get you to be in that state is really detrimental
too,"* she continues.

Oh yes. This I recall from school. A doctor that was teaching
that particular class told us that during stressful situations

like that, the adrenal glands release massive amounts of stress hormones like cortisol and adrenaline. The brain makes sure that all blood is rerouted from the digestive system to the muscles to give them what they need in case they need to act, like run or fight back. Blood pressure and heart rate both increase as do the core temperature and sweating.

Textbook fight or flight response.

"You want to put that kind of stress on your body? Especially after you had a you know what?" asks Inner Me, avoiding using the word 'stroke'.

"I hope you're no longer wondering why you ended up having a stroke," Ego says. No filter as always.

His words sting, but they are full of truth. My constant fearful thoughts, angry thoughts and thoughts of evening the score never served me well.

I am silent, absorbing all this. Though it's nothing new, having read it in numerous books before, coming from my very being has a different impact.

"I know doing all that was horrible. It never felt good, or satisfying as you say, to yell at someone, to fight with someone, to be scared, to be angry, to be judgemental. None of it ever felt good. But I felt like it was the only way to express how I felt, you know – mad, angry, offended, afraid..." I reply to Inner Me, ignoring Ego's remark.

"What made you feel mad, angry and afraid?" she asks.

"Well, mostly people. People, situations.... you know..." I respond, trailing off.

"How would people and situations make you mad or angry?" she asks, digging deeper.

"Or afraid?" adds Ego.

208

"By not being nice to me, by lying to me, by disrespecting me."

"Why do you think they would do that to you?" continues Inner Me.

"Because they probably don't think I am worth those things. You know, being told the truth, or being given respect, or being kind to, being patient with. Things like that." I say, tears welling up in my eyes again, the pain of those experiences rushing to the surface.

"Does it serve you well to think that you are not worthy? Does it feel good? Pleasing? Satisfying?" asks Inner Me, gentle and soft.

"No, of course not," I say, reaching for the tissue box on the nightstand.

"Well, if your life's dream and purpose is to be happy, where in that dream and purpose does the idea and the thought 'I'm not worthy' actually fit?" she continues with the questions.

It doesn't fit, I know.

I'm silent, but she continues. *"Why do you spend time giving attention to those kinds of thoughts as if they are true and factual?"*

"Because that's how I grew up. That was reality and it stared me in the face every day. In essence it was the truth of my life," I respond, sadness washing over me at the memories of life in communism.

A Worthy State of Mind

I had never actually sat back to think in detail about my worthiness or unworthiness. It's just there, in me. Back home in Romania the government didn't think I, or my family, or many of the people that lived there for that matter, were worthy of being given access to adequate food, or electricity or water. Everything was scarce. Only **some** people had everything in abundance. They were all in high-ranking positions and usually involved in the oppression. Us common folk weren't deemed worthy. Not even of being told the truth about things that took place in the rest of the world. Having that be daily life for years on end kind of brainwashed me into believing it all as truth.

That truth spilled into other areas of life, like personal relationships – unworthy of being told the truth, unworthy of loyalty, unworthy of being accepted…. Simply unworthy. It sort of became part of my being.

"Okay, now that you have identified where this silly unworthiness stems from, let's get rid of it," says Ego full of enthusiasm.

"Oh dear Simone, we are your cheerleaders and biggest fans, and you know, there are so many people in your life who are too. And yet here you are, your worst and harshest critic, telling yourself things that are simply not true. You've practiced doing this so much that you have made it into a habit," says Inner Me gently.

She is so right on. I have been practicing all that daily. Multiple times a day. Countless times really.

"Yes, you are working against yourself and what you want, and you know it. You are doing this to yourself," adds Ego.

"Remember that time when you went for lunch with your two friends from school and one of them offered to pay for your lunch?"

I recall that lunch. I always loved spending time with the girls from Nutrition school. We were all like-minded and always on the same page. We shared our journeys that brought us to studying what we were studying. We had all become soul sisters that had just found each other.

*"Do you remember what your response was? "Oh no, it's okay, I'll pay for myself." She clearly thought you were worthy of a lunch, but **you** certainly didn't think you were worthy of someone buying you lunch, did you? See? You work against yourself,"* says Inner Me. *"You make up all kinds of things as to why you are not worthy, even when people around you think that you are."*

That's true. Those girls accepted me and embraced me unconditionally. We shared notes, helped each other with assignments and invited each other over. I was brought into the private lives of these amazing souls….I went to their homes, met their significant others and held their babies.

"You turning down that girl offering to buy you lunch is proof that it's you that's working against yourself. Like I said earlier, it starts with you and it ends with you," she adds.

"Okay yes, but what about people that hurt me? Lied to me? Deceived me? Betrayed me? They did that all by themselves, no one held a gun to their heads," I ask, thoughts of those who had not been so kind to me rushing to make themselves known. Painful experiences are certainly not something you forget. Anything you are involved with emotionally is forever etched into your soul.

"Oh, Simone, they just don't know any better. Most people just regurgitate what they saw in their life growing up, what they learned. It's all they know, so it's all they can offer. It has nothing to do with you, and everything to do with them. They didn't do any of those things to hurt you." Inner Me answers.

"And you know that you lied to the whole world about your pain. You pretended you were okay when you and Frank split up. You put on such a show of strength and resilience. But that wasn't the truth, was it Simone?" she continues, gentleness and kindness in her words.

"No, no it wasn't," I say as tears start to roll down my cheeks, the pain of that time welling up inside me and coming to the very front of my awareness.

*"You didn't have a master plan to lie to the world; you did it because you had been taught to keep that kind of pain to yourself and not to talk about it. You did what you learned. Well these people who lied to you did the same – they acted according to what **they** learned."*

Being part of me, she knows that I never planned to lie to the world just so that I can be malicious, or to hurt people. I did do it because it's what was acceptable. Talking about your plight was just not cool. And my need to always look strong was the driving force behind those lies. Looking weak was a sin in my books, so my massive lie was justified.

She goes on, *"Can you now understand why you must forgive yourself and others for all the mistakes and misgivings? Everyone acts in accordance with what they know and what they learned. You included."*

"Yes," I whisper, as memories of how broken and afraid I was back then envelop me.

"When you felt justified to yell, to fight, to swear, you were acting from the very limitation of your thinking about what's appropriate and what's justified. It's what you learned. Even if it's uncalled for and unnecessary, doing all that is appropriate and justified to you. Everyone says and does things that are appropriate and justified to them."

"Do you understand?" she asks.

"Yes."

"See? You get it," she says, kind and soft as always.

I did get it. In fact it was more of a realization than anything else. That knowledge and that wisdom was all inside me. I had merely ignored my own inner wisdom, because I had been distracted by things.....by everyday life.

It was no secret to me or to Inner Me and Ego that back home during the brutal communist regime that I grew up in, I learned to lie really really well. To my parents, to my aunts and uncles, to my grandparents and even to school teachers. In that culture, during those times, everyone had the freedom to hit children. Teachers in particular, who were pushing forward the communist agenda through everything they taught, hit their students liberally. Hit, as in physically assaulting them. Which they did as they saw fit.

One year, my dad (aka the biggest badass, alpha male in the country) brought home oranges. Oranges were unheard of in Romania among us regular folk. We were limited to the rationed food from the government and whatever we grew in our own gardens. None of my friends had ever even laid eyes on an orange, much less tasted one. I decided to take one to school with me and share it with my closest girlfriends.

During break between classes, I peeled the orange and meticulously divided it so that all my girlfriends had a piece. It was a real delicacy and a treat. This, of course, made me very popular among my classmates. Next class was math, taught by a very elegant but incredibly harsh woman, who just happened to be pregnant at the time. She walked in and got the scent of the orange. Whether it nauseated her or triggered a craving remains a mystery. She asked what the smell was and what caused it. Fearing her wrath, which she was notorious for, I kept silent, as did all my friends and classmates. We were all scared of her. Though she asked the question repeatedly, each time, she was met with silence. I prayed that since she didn't identify the culprit, she would put the issue to rest and do what she was there to do, teach us the intricacies of math. But no, instead, in true communist fashion, she punished us all. We were ordered to stand and hold our hands out, palms facing up. She then proceeded to take a metal ruler and walk around hitting our hands with the sharp edge, asking each one of us "Was it you?", her words and her voice full of anger. All of us, though innocent, were punished for doing absolutely nothing wrong.

My only saving grace was that I had washed my hands after peeling the orange, so that I can remove the stickiness and staining of the peel off my hands.

Defiant as I had been since young, after a few hits, I dared respond to her "No, it wasn't me. It wasn't any of us."

This earned me a trip to the Principal's office, with a complimentary promise to notify my parents of my antics and audacity to answer back, which was a cardinal sin in every school.

And thus, my habit of lying to avoid punishment was born. During the formative years when it goes straight into the subconscious mind, no less. I would practice and reinforce this habit throughout my life, and use it liberally, especially to avoid hurting the feelings of others.

We lie to our parents, to our spouses, our lovers, our friends, our bosses and even our children; sometimes for very good reasons – can we say Santa, Easter Bunny and Tooth Fairy??

"I'm so happy you understand Simone. These things are part of life. You are worthy, of course you are. Everyone makes mistakes, you included. The magic is in not letting your thoughts and feelings about these mistakes be tied to your worth," she continues.

Truth is I always let my thoughts and my feelings about mistakes - my own and those of others - be tied to my worth. And as a result, I always reacted, instead of responding.

"Do not let those thoughts and feelings take up residence in the sacred place that is your soul. Do not carry all that inside of you. Let it all go. Forgive others for making

mistakes and forgive yourself too," she adds, in her signature gentle way.

I sat in silence absorbing all this, letting it seep deep into the depths of my mind, so that I could dismantle the web of bullshit that it had constructed and trapped me into for all these decades.

It all made sense now. The dots were connected and the pieces fit together in my mind like pieces in a game of Tetris. All gaps were now filled. The whole wall of unworthiness bullshit crumbled in my mind. And with it went the guilt, the bad feelings, the thoughts of *'I can't believe she did this to me'* or *'How could he do that?'*

I was done; finally, free of the heaviest burden I had carried my entire life - lack of self-worth. I removed the root of it all, ensuring that it will never grow in the garden of my mind.

I know that people will betray me again; some will lie, others will be deceptive, cruel, mean, cunning, and that I will feel anger, disappointment, sadness, grief and even shame again at some point. I know that thoughts will come in packs and that I will have to deal with them....to keep them at bay....to eliminate them. I know that it will be tiring; even exhausting. But it doesn't matter anymore. I just learned the most priceless life lesson - that people's mistakes are part of the process of life and that what all those people did to me is all they knew and all they had learned. I now have the blueprint of a happy life. No matter how much work it will involve, it will be worth it. And Inner Me and Ego will always be there to help me.

"Why didn't you tell me all this sooner?" I ask.

"You weren't ready," says Inner Me.

"How was I ready now?" I continue with my questions.

"You had the desire and intent to ask yourself questions. And you were willing to listen for the answers," she responds.

"I always wanted answers."

"You never looked inside for the answers, you always sought them outside of yourself," she says calmly.

She continues. *"Don't think that the answers you found tonight end your work. Your work must continue. Much like how you have to continue with a healthy diet and a healthy lifestyle to maintain good physical health, you will have to continue with directing your thoughts to positive things and always think about things being as you want them to be, not as they are and definitely not as the way you **don't** want them to be,"* she urges me, knowing that I understand the importance of investing in things long-term.

"Remember, you are always in charge of your life," she adds.

*"Ugh, you're right! I always think about how I **don't** want things to be. I guess I'm constantly thinking about negative things and how I want to avoid them,"* I say, realizing about my constant attention to the negative aspects of things.

Everything makes sense now. You can only heal what you become aware of. And you can only become aware if you ask yourself questions. The way I have been thinking manifested the good and bad things in my life, including the stroke and the divorce. The power of my thoughts. The way I've reacted to life-events and to things that people have said or done. And what a difference responding instead of reacting really makes.

I've never liked the idea of doing things like everybody else, just because.....well, just because I'm me. Why should I start now? I've tried so hard to blend in when I'm clearly meant to stand out! Yes, people are conditioned to think negative because this is how they survived in caves. Or in communist regimes. But there have always been people who were looking for that thriving life outside the cave....outside communism.....outside the current system. My dad was one of them. I, too, am one of them. Every single one of us has an opportunity to find a way, to push through pain and fear, to recondition ourselves, and to learn how to respond, rather than react. Nobody can think positive thoughts for us, and nobody can make us feel worthy if we don't believe we are.

And so here in this moment, I decide to feel worthy. For the rest of my life.

"Because you are," says Ego.

I wish I could hug these two parts of my being - Inner Me and Ego. I'm so grateful for them, for their presence and their guidance. I finally get the true sense of pure self-love everybody has been talking about.

"Thank you for all you have ever done and continue to do. I am so grateful for you two. I love you both so much," I say, feelings of unadulterated love flowing from the depth of me.

"We love you too Simone. More than you know. And we will always be with you to help you and to guide you. Always," says Inner Me oozing love herself.

"Yeah, I must say, sometimes I wish I were you," says Ego.

"Wait. I am you," he adds laughing.

"Whatever. I always knew the world is your oyster baby. And that we can make shit happen," he continues, in true Ego fashion.

"Can we talk about that Porsche now?" he asks. *"I say baby blue. Or yellow if you want. 911 GT1. Twenty-one-inch rims, low profile tires,"* he adds, excitement in his tone.

I smile at the thought and close my eyes, momentarily seeing myself driving the very car he just described. It's a beautiful sight. But I decide not to answer. There's something I'd like to do now more than getting the Porsche. And they both know it as well as I do. It's time to face the obvious.

"I can totally do this!" I say, calmness in my voice, smiling ear to ear.

"Of COURSE, you can do it," says Ego, knowing exactly what I am referring to.

"Yes, yes you can Simone," adds Inner Me, full of encouragement.

*"Oh, so many have done it. Thousands, in fact hundreds of thousands.....wait, no, **millions** of people have written a book. There is absolutely no reason why you can't do it. You got through the divorce, and the stroke like a boss. A boss baby, a boss!! A book is like a walk in the park,"* continues Ego, almost exasperated that he has to state the obvious.

He's right. Millions of people write books and get published every year. And through those books they help other people. Now I'm about to be one of them. If they can do it, so can I. It's time to fully complete the healing.

"Let's do this," I say excitedly, sitting down in front of my laptop.

About the Author ♡

Simone Gisondi is a Certified Holistic Nutritional Consultant, Regenerative Detoxification Specialist, Holistic Cancer Practitioner and Certified Hypnotist. She educates, coaches and mentors others on how to restore their health and tap into the body's natural healing process by using her 3-pronged holistic health solution for energy, vitality and disease reversal.

Simone heads her own holistic health practice with a focus on nutritional intervention for chronic disease reversal and optimizing long term health. She has earned the Holistic Nutrition Consultant and Holistic Cancer Practitioner certificates in Canada and completed her Holistic Cancer Care internship at the Marsden Centre for Excellence in Integrative Medicine.

She emigrated to North America with her family at the age of 12, is a mom of two and currently lives in Florida, USA. Aside from health, her passion is writing and painting.

Review This Book ♡

It means the world to me that you purchased my book.

Writing is my passion and I look forward to YOUR feedback.

So if you liked this book, I'd like to ask for a small favor. Would you be so kind to leave a review on Amazon?

I'd very much appreciate it!

If you'd like to learn more about me and receive my FREE Meal Plan, please head to my website -

https://www.simonegisondi.com/resources-download

With Gratitude,

Simone

Printed in Great Britain
by Amazon